Fractions, Decimals, Percentages

Fractions 5

Teacher's Guide

Hilary Koll and Steve Mills

Schofield & Sims

Free downloads available from the Schofield & Sims website

A selection of free downloads is available from the Schofield & Sims website (www.schofieldandsims.co.uk/free-downloads). These may be used to further enhance the effectiveness of the programme. The downloads add to the range of print materials supplied in the teacher's guides.

- **Graphics** slides containing the visual elements from each teacher's guide unit provided as Microsoft PowerPoint® presentations.

- **Go deeper investigations** providing additional extension material to develop problem-solving and reasoning skills.

- **Additional resources** including a fraction wall, a comparison chart and number lines to support learning and teaching.

Published by **Schofield & Sims Ltd**, Dogley Mill, Fenay Bridge, Huddersfield HD8 0NQ, UK
Telephone 01484 607080
www.schofieldandsims.co.uk

This edition copyright © Schofield & Sims Ltd, 2017
First published in 2017

Authors: **Hilary Koll and Steve Mills**
Hilary Koll and Steve Mills have asserted their moral rights under the Copyright, Designs and Patents Act, 1988, to be identified as the authors of this work.

British Library Cataloguing in Publication Data
A catalogue record for this book is available from the British Library.

Design by **Oxford Designers & Illustrators Ltd**
Printed in the UK by **Page Bros (Norwich) Ltd**

ISBN 978 07217 1384 7

Contents

Introduction

Overview

Fractions, decimals and percentages are frequent areas of difficulty in mathematics for primary school pupils. Many teachers find them challenging to teach and pupils often have limited or only partially developed conceptual understanding of the topics. A major reason children struggle with fractions, decimals and percentages is the variety of contexts and representations in which they appear – for example, as areas, as sets, on number lines, as a result of a division problem and in relation to measurements.

Schofield & Sims Fractions, Decimals and Percentages is a structured whole-school programme designed to help pupils develop a deep, secure and adaptable understanding of these topics. The series consists of six pupil books and six teacher's guides, one for each primary school year.

Each unit of the programme addresses a single learning objective. The teacher's guides provide detailed teaching notes with accompanying graphics to use in lessons. The pupil books provide a summary of the learning objective and a set of related practice questions that increase in difficulty. This allows you, the teacher or adult helper, to introduce and teach a particular concept and then to provide appropriate intelligent practice which gradually leads children towards more complex representations and varied contexts.

Supporting a mastery approach, all pupils are encouraged to move at the same pace through the units and are given the same opportunity to fully understand the concept being taught. Depth of learning is emphasised over speed of learning and the pupils should have a solid understanding of the content of each unit before moving on to new material. Downloadable **Go deeper** extension resources help to cement pupils' understanding of the concepts that have been taught. The series also provides ongoing and integrated assessment throughout.

Prerequisites for Fractions 5

Before beginning **Fractions 5** the pupils should:

- have an understanding of unit and non-unit fractions and how to compare, add and subtract fractions with the same denominator

- be familiar with mixed numbers and appreciate that improper fractions are greater than one whole

- have an understanding of decimals with up to two decimal places and know their relationship to tenths and hundredths.

Each year of the programme, however, begins with revision to ensure that the pupils understand the necessary ideas to move forward. The pupils can be given **Fractions 4** first if they require further practice to build their confidence and their understanding.

The focus in Year 5 is on the following areas: comparing and ordering fractions, equivalent fractions, mixed numbers, improper fractions, percentages, multiplying proper fractions and mixed numbers by whole numbers, writing decimals as fractions, rounding decimals to one decimal place, and problem solving.

Fractions 5 and the National Curriculum

Fractions 5 and its related **Teacher's Guide** match the statutory requirements for Year 5 for 'Fractions (including decimals and percentages)' in the National Curriculum. The 12 statutory requirements are listed on the following page. They have been coded for ease of reference. For example, Y5/F1 refers to the first fractions requirement in Year 5.

National Curriculum requirements for 'Fractions (including decimals and percentages)'

Y5/F1 Compare and order fractions whose denominators are all multiples of the same number.

Y5/F2 Identify, name and write equivalent fractions of a given fraction, represented visually, including tenths and hundredths.

Y5/F3 Recognise mixed numbers and improper fractions and convert from one form to the other and write mathematical statements >1 as a mixed number (for example, $\frac{2}{5} + \frac{4}{5} = \frac{6}{5} = 1\frac{1}{5}$).

Y5/F4 Add and subtract fractions with the same denominator, and denominators that are multiples of the same number.

Y5/F5 Multiply proper fractions and mixed numbers by whole numbers, supported by materials and diagrams.

Y5/F6 Read and write decimal numbers as fractions (for example, $0.71 = \frac{71}{100}$).

Y5/F7 Recognise and use thousandths and relate them to tenths, hundredths and decimal equivalents.

Y5/F8 Round decimals with two decimal places to the nearest whole number and to one decimal place.

Y5/F9 Read, write, order and compare numbers with up to three decimal places.

Y5/F10 Solve problems involving numbers with up to three decimal places.

Y5/F11 Recognise the per cent symbol (%) and understand that per cent relates to 'number of parts per 100', and write percentages as a fraction with denominator 100, and as a decimal fraction.

Y5/F12 Solve problems which require knowing percentage and decimal equivalents of $\frac{1}{2}, \frac{1}{4}, \frac{1}{5}, \frac{2}{5}, \frac{4}{5}$ and those fractions with a denominator of a multiple of 10 or 25.

The National Curriculum coverage chart on page 6 maps all the units and tests in **Fractions 5** against the National Curriculum requirements. When reading the chart, please refer to the curriculum coding introduced above. The light shaded boxes show where a requirement is touched upon and the dark shaded boxes show the key units and tests for that requirement. The first column, labelled 'Y4 Revision', shows the units that revise Year 4 material.

National Curriculum coverage chart

	Y4 Revision	Y5/F1	Y5/F2	Y5/F3	Y5/F4	Y5/F5	Y5/F6	Y5/F7	Y5/F8	Y5/F9	Y5/F10	Y5/F11	Y5/F12
Unit 1	■		■										
Unit 2	■		■										
Unit 3				■									
Unit 4				■									
Unit 5				■	■								
Unit 6			■		■								
Check-up test 1			■	■	■								
Unit 7		■	■										
Unit 8	■	■	■			■							
Unit 9			■	■	■	■							
Unit 10			■			■							
Unit 11							■		■				
Unit 12							■	■		■			
Check-up test 2		■		■		■	■	■	■				
Unit 13										■	■		
Unit 14										■			
Unit 15												■	■
Unit 16												■	■
Unit 17			■			■							■
Unit 18			■	■		■	■				■	■	■
Check-up test 3			■		■					■	■	■	
Final test		■	■	■	■	■	■	■	■	■	■	■	■

Fractions 5 Teacher's Guide

The **Fractions 5 Teacher's Guide** contains everything you need to teach the National Curriculum requirements for 'Fractions (including decimals and percentages)' in Year 5. There are 18 corresponding units in the teacher's guide and pupil book, six for each term.

Using the Teacher's notes

In this teacher's guide you will find **Teacher's notes** for each unit (pages 12 to 47). These include a detailed lesson plan with accompanying graphics that can be used to demonstrate the learning objective before the pupils begin the activities in the pupil book. The graphics are visual prompts for the class and can be used in a variety of ways. They are all available as interactive PowerPoint® presentations (free to download from the Schofield & Sims website). Alternatively, the graphics could be presented on a projector, or photocopied and used as pupil handouts, or used as a guide when drawing your own visual prompts. The lesson plans can be easily adapted to suit your classroom. Below is an example lesson from this teacher's guide, alongside the corresponding slides from the **Fractions 5** PowerPoint® presentation.

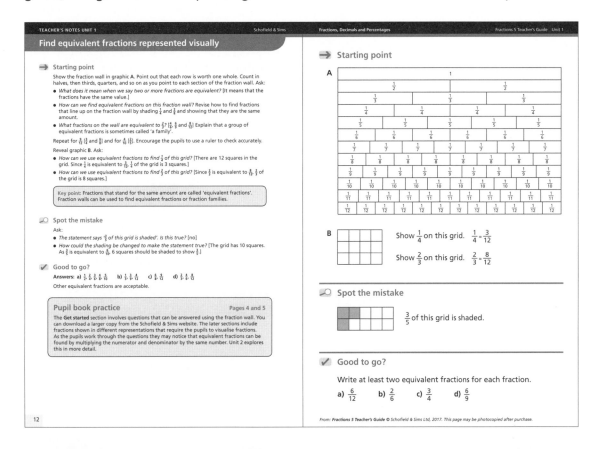

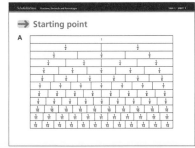

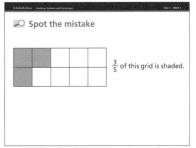

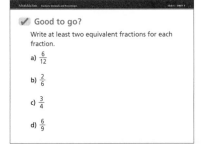

The **Teacher's notes** for each unit are divided into the following sections:

- **Starting point** – This section provides clear instruction on how to introduce and teach the learning objective. Using the graphics as prompts, probing questions are given that draw on the pupils' prior knowledge and encourage them to find connections, reason and reach conclusions about why the concept being taught is true. The **Key point** of the lesson is clearly highlighted.

- **Spot the mistake** – This is a statement, often with a visual element, that represents a mistake which is commonly made with the concept being taught. The statement is intentionally incorrect. You are given a series of corrective questions to ask the pupils, drawing out potential misconceptions and helping them to spot the mistake. Procedural understanding is deepened as the pupils discuss why the statement is incorrect and what the correct statement should be.

- **Good to go?** – This section has quick practice questions that help you establish whether each pupil has understood the lesson and is a useful tool for formative assessment. It is suggested that the pupils answer these questions on mini-whiteboards and hold up their answers. This helps you to quickly identify the pupils who require further assistance and those who have fully understood the unit focus.

- **Pupil book practice** – This section provides links to the pupil book pages for this unit. It flags potential areas of difficulty to be aware of in the activities, highlights when questions act as a bridge to later units, and offers further suggestions for practical resources you can use to support the pupils as they work.

Answers

The teacher's guide contains a complete set of **Answers** (pages 48 to 93) for all the units and tests in the pupil book. The answers are presented as correctly completed pupil book pages to make marking quick and easy.

Fractions 5 Pupil Book

Once you are confident that the pupils have grasped the concept of the lesson, they should turn to the corresponding unit in their pupil book. This offers varied activities of increasing difficulty that provide plenty of repetition, practice and challenge to consolidate learning.

The pupil book begins with a simple introduction which clearly explains the purpose of the book and how it is used. This introduction supports your own instructions for the pupils as they start this book. It is also a useful reference for parents if you decide to set sections of the pupil book as homework. Below is an example lesson from the pupil book.

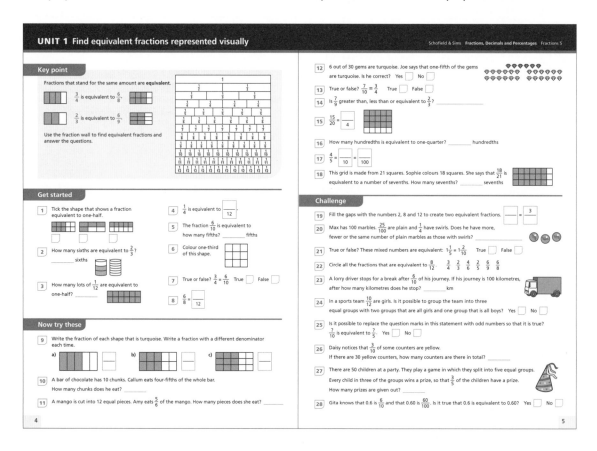

Each unit in the pupil book begins with a child-friendly summary of the **Key point** of the lesson, as a reminder for the pupil and to assist parents in supporting their children at home.

The practice questions in each unit are divided into three sections:

- **Get started** – Quick questions to help the pupil gain confidence in the topic, with a variety of straightforward practice questions related to the learning objective.
- **Now try these** – Additional number and practical problems to take the topic further with more varied vocabulary and representations.
- **Challenge** – Problem-solving questions involving greater challenge such as measurement and money contexts and links to other more complex concepts.

The pupils should write their answers directly into their own pupil book. Each completed pupil book provides a permanent record of achievement and encourages the pupils to take pride in their work. Three **Check-up tests**, one for the end of each term, a **Final test** and a **How did I find it?** checklist are also included in each pupil book. These help you to monitor the pupils' progress.

Strategies for learning

If a pupil is struggling with a question, prompt them to try it again using a different strategy. Problem-solving strategies develop deeper mathematical thinking, allowing pupils to solve a wider variety of problems.

- **Visualising** – *Sketch a picture of the situation or use real-life objects to model it.*
- **Simplifying** – *If a problem seems too difficult, make it easier. For example, change decimals into whole numbers, and work out how you would solve the easier problem. Then go back to the harder problem and see if you can find the answer.*
- **Using trial and improvement** – *It can help to guess what the answer might be. Look at the question again, with the guessed number in mind, and see how your guess needs to be changed. Sometimes you can get an idea of whether the answer is larger or smaller than your guess. Choose an adjusted number and keep repeating this until you get to the right answer.*
- **Reasoning** – *Discuss the problem with a partner and make suggestions such as 'If you tried adding, would that work?' or 'Do you think dividing would give us the answer?'. Suggestions don't have to be right but they can really help to get you thinking.*
- **Looking for patterns** – *Look out for patterns in the numbers in a problem. Sometimes you can find an answer by spotting a pattern and continuing it.*
- **Generalising** – *Some problems involve thinking of an idea more generally or saying whether a statement is never, sometimes or always true. For this you must generalise. This means thinking carefully about an idea in lots of different situations.*
- **Checking** – *Go back and check your answers. You could use inverse operations or work backwards from the answer. Make sure you haven't made any wrong assumptions.*
- **Persevering** – *When all else fails, keep going! Try using a coloured pen to highlight the important numbers in the problem and see if that helps you to spot a pattern.*

Go deeper

When teaching for mastery, differentiation is achieved by emphasising depth of knowledge and mathematical fluency over pace of learning. The **Challenge** questions in the pupil book offer sophisticated problems that will stretch even the more able student and provide the practice that is required to exceed the expected national standards. **Go deeper investigations** are also available (free to download from the Schofield & Sims website), which correspond with the content covered up to each **Check-up test**. These group work problem-solving activities help pupils to delve even more deeply into the concepts being taught and cement their understanding. Teacher's notes and pupil worksheets are provided for each investigation. These can be used with the whole class in a dedicated problem-solving lesson or as extension material for pupils who require further challenge.

Assessment

Fractions 5 and its related **Teacher's Guide** offer frequent opportunities and multiple resources for in-school assessment. These resources should be used in line with your school's own assessment policy.

Formative assessment

The teacher's guide lesson plans all feature precise questioning. This can be used as part of your ongoing formative assessment to test the pupils' conceptual and procedural knowledge. The questions can help to uncover a pupil's reasoning and depth of mathematical thinking. The **Good to go?** section at the end of each lesson provides a further check, enabling you to easily identify when pupils are struggling and when they are ready to progress to the pupil book practice questions.

The pupil book units can also be used as a basis for formative assessment. Teachers should monitor the progress that each pupil is making as they work through the pupil book questions. If an answer is incorrect, asking the pupil to explain how they reached this answer may reveal gaps in understanding that can then be addressed.

Three **Check-up tests** are provided in the pupil book. These can be used to test the pupils' understanding of the material covered in the preceding six units. This allows you to ascertain how well the pupils have remembered the ideas covered in the programme so far and how secure their understanding is.

Each pupil's day-to-day progress can be monitored by using the **Pupil progress chart** (at the back of this book). This chart can be photocopied for each pupil in your class so that you can keep track of the marks scored on each unit and **Check-up test**. Guidance is provided below on how to interpret the information gained from the **Pupil progress chart**.

Decoding the unit scores

While the total score achieved in each pupil book unit will be a good indicator of the pupils' overall progress, it is advisable to keep an eye out for patterns in their scores across the three different sections as well.

- If a pupil struggles with **Get started**, it can indicate that the pupil has not yet understood or has misunderstood the concept of the unit and is likely to require further support.

- If a pupil struggles with **Now try these** after a successful **Get started**, it can indicate that the pupil has understood the initial idea but is having trouble applying it to different contexts and with different representations.

- If a pupil struggles with **Challenge** after a successful **Get started** and **Now try these**, it can indicate that the pupil may need further help in problem-solving processes such as reasoning, simplifying, visualising, looking for patterns or generalising. It may also indicate that the pupil is having difficulty with comprehension skills, misunderstanding the language that is used in the question.

- If the pupil is able to make a good attempt at **Challenge** after a successful **Get started** and **Now try these**, it can indicate that the pupil has mastered the unit and is secure in their understanding of the concepts that have been taught.

- If the pupil scores highly across all three sections, it can indicate that the pupil has mastered the concepts of the unit at greater depth.

- Look out for inconsistent scoring across the sections, for example, a low score in **Get started** and a high score in **Now try these** or a low score in **Now try these** and a high score in **Challenge** as this may mean that there are gaps in the pupil's understanding. Some guesswork may have been involved in gaining correct answers.

> ### Decoding the Check-up test scores
>
> - A score of 0–17 can indicate that the pupil has not yet understood all of the key concepts in the preceding units. Further consolidation work or a different approach may be needed to ensure secure understanding.
>
> - A score of 18–24 can indicate that the pupil has mastered the concepts of the preceding units and can confidently move forward.

Each pupil book also contains a **How did I find it?** checklist which enables the pupils to evaluate their own progress as they work through the programme. Each unit has a corresponding 'I can' statement. After completing each unit, **Check-up test** and **Final test** the pupils should be given the opportunity to rate how they found the unit – 'difficult', 'getting there' or 'easy'.

Summative assessment

The **Final test** in the pupil book can be used for in-school summative assessment at the end of **Fractions 5**. This test allows you to assess the pupils' understanding of all the concepts covered in **Fractions 5**. The **Final test** is organised so that each section tests a different statutory requirement for the Year 5 National Curriculum.

Marks for the **Final test** can be recorded on the **Final test group record sheet** (at the back of this book). Record each mark by either ticking or shading the relevant boxes next to each pupil's name. This chart outlines which curriculum requirement is being tested in each section using the curriculum coding that was introduced on page 5. It provides an at-a-glance overview of how the whole class is performing in relation to the National Curriculum requirements and enables you to evaluate pupil learning at the end of the year. Guidance is provided below on how to interpret the information gained from this chart.

> ### Decoding the Final test scores
>
> - A score of 0–26 marks can indicate that the pupil has not fully mastered the key concepts for the year. The curriculum coding should provide a clear idea of which requirements the pupil is struggling with. Catch-up work is likely to be needed in these areas before the pupil is ready to proceed with Year 6 material.
>
> - A score of 27–36 marks can indicate that the pupil has mastered the key concepts for the year and can confidently move forward to Year 6 material. The curriculum coding should provide a clear idea of the pupil's strengths and warn of any areas of weakness that may require additional practice in Year 6.

The **Final test group record sheet** provides a useful record for school leaders and inspectors and will show the subsequent teacher how secure each pupil was in their knowledge of the previous year's curriculum and how ready they are for progression.

Find equivalent fractions represented visually

➡️ Starting point

Show the fraction wall in graphic **A**. Point out that each row is worth one whole. Count in halves, then thirds, quarters, and so on as you point to each section of the fraction wall. Ask:

- *What does it mean when we say two or more fractions are equivalent?* [It means that the fractions have the same value.]
- *How can we find equivalent fractions on this fraction wall?* Revise how to find fractions that line up on the fraction wall by shading $\frac{1}{4}$ and $\frac{2}{8}$ and showing that they are the same amount.
- *What fractions on the wall are equivalent to $\frac{2}{3}$?* [$\frac{4}{6}$, $\frac{6}{9}$ and $\frac{8}{12}$] Explain that a group of equivalent fractions is sometimes called 'a family'.

Repeat for $\frac{9}{12}$ [$\frac{3}{4}$ and $\frac{6}{8}$] and for $\frac{4}{10}$ [$\frac{2}{5}$]. Encourage the pupils to use a ruler to check accurately.

Reveal graphic **B**. Ask:

- *How can we use equivalent fractions to find $\frac{1}{4}$ of this grid?* [There are 12 squares in the grid. Since $\frac{1}{4}$ is equivalent to $\frac{3}{12}$, $\frac{1}{4}$ of the grid is 3 squares.]
- *How can we use equivalent fractions to find $\frac{2}{3}$ of this grid?* [Since $\frac{2}{3}$ is equivalent to $\frac{8}{12}$, $\frac{2}{3}$ of the grid is 8 squares.]

> **Key point:** Fractions that stand for the same amount are called 'equivalent fractions'. Fraction walls can be used to find equivalent fractions or fraction families.

🔍 Spot the mistake

Ask:

- *The statement says '$\frac{3}{5}$ of this grid is shaded'. Is this true?* [no]
- *How could the shading be changed to make the statement true?* [The grid has 10 squares. As $\frac{3}{5}$ is equivalent to $\frac{6}{10}$, 6 squares should be shaded to show $\frac{3}{5}$.]

✔️ Good to go?

Answers: a) $\frac{1}{2}$, $\frac{2}{4}$, $\frac{3}{6}$, $\frac{4}{8}$, $\frac{5}{10}$ **b)** $\frac{1}{3}$, $\frac{3}{9}$, $\frac{4}{12}$ **c)** $\frac{6}{8}$, $\frac{9}{12}$ **d)** $\frac{2}{3}$, $\frac{4}{6}$, $\frac{8}{12}$

Other equivalent fractions are acceptable.

Pupil book practice   Pages 4 and 5

The **Get started** section involves questions that can be answered using the fraction wall. You can download a larger copy from the Schofield & Sims website. The later sections include fractions shown in different representations that require the pupils to visualise fractions. As the pupils work through the questions they may notice that equivalent fractions can be found by multiplying the numerator and denominator by the same number. Unit 2 explores this in more detail.

Starting point

A

1											

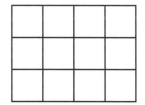

(Fraction wall showing bars divided into 1, halves, thirds, quarters, fifths, sixths, sevenths, eighths, ninths, tenths, elevenths and twelfths.)

B

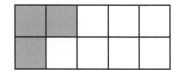

Show $\frac{1}{4}$ on this grid. $\frac{1}{4} = \frac{3}{12}$

Show $\frac{2}{3}$ on this grid. $\frac{2}{3} = \frac{8}{12}$

 Spot the mistake

$\frac{3}{5}$ of this grid is shaded.

✔ **Good to go?**

Write at least two equivalent fractions for each fraction.

a) $\frac{6}{12}$ b) $\frac{2}{6}$ c) $\frac{3}{4}$ d) $\frac{6}{9}$

Find equivalent fractions using patterns

➡️ **Starting point**

Show the first pair of equivalent fractions in graphic **A**. Ask:

- *Look at the two rectangles showing $\frac{9}{12}$ and $\frac{3}{4}$. Are the two fractions equivalent?* [yes] Explain that the numerator and the denominator of $\frac{9}{12}$ can both be divided by 3 to give the fraction $\frac{3}{4}$.

Look at the next three pairs of equivalent fractions in graphic **A**. Ask:

- *Do you see how the top and the bottom number have both been divided or multiplied by the same number to give an equivalent fraction?* Elicit descriptions of each relationship, for example, 'We can see that $\frac{3}{7}$ is equivalent to $\frac{15}{35}$ as both the numerator and denominator of $\frac{3}{7}$ have been multiplied by 5 to give $\frac{15}{35}$'.

Reveal the first pair of equivalent fractions in graphic **B**. Ask:

- *What is the missing number here, if both fractions are equivalent?* [100] *So what fraction is equivalent to $\frac{2}{5}$?* [$\frac{40}{100}$]

Then reveal the second pair of equivalent fractions. Ask:

- *What must we divide both numbers by to go from eighty-eighths to eighths?* [11]
- *How many eighths is equivalent to $\frac{77}{88}$?* [$\frac{7}{8}$] Ensure the pupils understand that both numbers must be multiplied or divided by the same number, but that the value of the fraction itself does not change.

> **Key point:** If both the numerator and denominator of a fraction are multiplied or divided by the same number, an equivalent fraction is always produced.

🔍 **Spot the mistake**

- *The statement says '$\frac{3}{5} = \frac{80}{100}$'. Are these two fractions equivalent?* [no]
- *What is the mistake?* [The denominator has been multiplied by 20 to get hundredths, but the numerator has not been multiplied by 20.]
- *What fraction with the denominator 100 is equivalent to $\frac{3}{5}$?* [$\frac{60}{100}$]

✔️ **Good to go?**

Answers: a) 30   **b)** 35   **c)** 10

Pupil book practice   Pages 6 and 7

Pupils often find it hard to grasp that fractions written with different numbers have the same value as each other and that multiplying or dividing both numbers leaves the value unchanged. If the pupils find these ideas too difficult, again provide them with fraction walls and encourage them to use diagrams to solve the problems. It is not vital for Year 5 pupils to master the more abstract processes at this stage but, if they can manage it, it is a really useful way for them to check their work and gain confidence with equivalence. In **Challenge**, the pupils are asked to simplify several fractions. Though they are not expected to simplify all their answers at this stage, this is a good opportunity to remind the pupils that simplifying gives a better answer.

→ Starting point

A

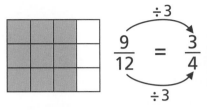

$$\frac{9}{12} \overset{\div 3}{\underset{\div 3}{=}} \frac{3}{4}$$

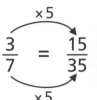

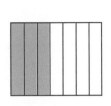

$$\frac{3}{7} \overset{\times 5}{\underset{\times 5}{=}} \frac{15}{35}$$

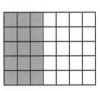

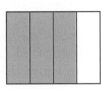

$$\frac{100}{300} \overset{\div 100}{\underset{\div 100}{=}} \frac{1}{3}$$

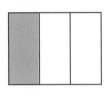

$$\frac{5}{8} \overset{\times 12}{\underset{\times 12}{=}} \frac{60}{96}$$

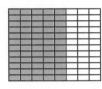

B

$$\frac{2}{5} \overset{\times 20}{\underset{\times 20}{=}} \frac{40}{\boxed{}}$$

$$\frac{77}{88} \overset{\div \boxed{}}{\underset{\div \boxed{}}{=}} \frac{\boxed{}}{8}$$

🔍 Spot the mistake

$$\frac{3}{5} = \frac{80}{100}$$

✔ Good to go?

Complete these equivalent fractions.

a) $\frac{3}{10} = \dfrac{\boxed{}}{100}$

b) $\frac{7}{9} = \dfrac{\boxed{}}{45}$

c) $\frac{27}{30} = \dfrac{9}{\boxed{}}$

Convert from mixed numbers to improper fractions

➡️ **Starting point**

Display the number line in graphic **A**. Ask:

- *How many equal parts is each whole on this number line divided into?* [5] Draw attention to the fact that there are 4 marks between each whole number on the line but that this represents 5 intervals, as shown by the rectangles above the number line.

Show the first two questions. Ask:

- *How many fifths are equal to one whole?* [5]
- *How many fifths are equal to two wholes?* [10]

Then reveal the mixed number question and ask:

- *What do we call a number that has a whole number and a fraction?* [a mixed number]
- *How many fifths are equal to the mixed number 'two and three-fifths'? How can you find out?* Prompt the pupils to notice that you can multiply the whole number by 5 and then add the extra $\frac{3}{5}$ to give the answer. [$\frac{13}{5}$]

Repeat for graphic **B**. After exploring the whole numbers, lead the pupils to notice that you can multiply the whole number 3 by the denominator 8 to find how many eighths are in 3 wholes and then add the extra $\frac{1}{8}$ to give the answer $\frac{25}{8}$. Ask:

- *What do we call a top-heavy fraction like this where the numerator is larger than the denominator?* [an improper fraction]

Provide further mixed numbers and invite the pupils to convert them to improper fractions, for example $5\frac{4}{5}$, $1\frac{5}{8}$, $3\frac{3}{4}$ and $4\frac{2}{3}$. [$\frac{29}{5}$, $\frac{13}{8}$, $\frac{15}{4}$, $\frac{14}{3}$] Each time, ask the pupils to describe their method of calculation.

> **Key point:** To write a mixed number as an improper fraction, multiply the whole number by the denominator and then add the numerator. This gives the numerator of the improper fraction. The denominator remains the same.

🔍 **Spot the mistake**

Ask:

- *The statement says '$1\frac{4}{5} = \frac{8}{5}$'. Is this true?* [no]
- *What is $1\frac{4}{5}$ written as an improper fraction?* [$\frac{9}{5}$]

✅ **Good to go?**

Answers: a) $\frac{17}{5}$ **b)** $\frac{5}{3}$ **c)** $\frac{19}{8}$ **d)** $\frac{31}{10}$

> ## Pupil book practice   Pages 8 and 9
>
> The pupils should practise saying how many of each unit fraction make up a whole number, for example $\frac{4}{4}$ = 1 whole, $\frac{8}{8}$ = 1 whole, $\frac{8}{4}$ = 2 wholes, $\frac{16}{8}$ = 2 wholes etc. They should do this with a range of fractions. In this way, they can begin to appreciate why multiplication is necessary. The early questions focus on whole numbers and, if any pupils struggle with later work, they should be given more of this type of practice. Some of the **Challenge** questions involve converting tenths and hundredths from mixed numbers to improper fractions. Explain to the pupils that in these instances the same digits appear in both the mixed number and the related improper fraction, for example $4\frac{8}{10} = \frac{48}{10}$ or $5\frac{34}{100} = \frac{534}{100}$. However, it is important for the pupils to realise that these are special cases and the pattern does not work for other fractions.

→ Starting point

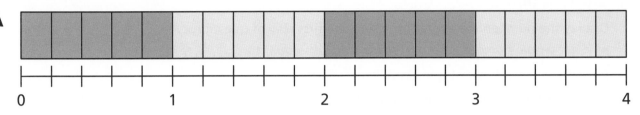

A

$1 =$ ☐ fifths

$2 =$ ☐ fifths

$2\frac{3}{5} =$ ☐ fifths $= \dfrac{☐}{5}$

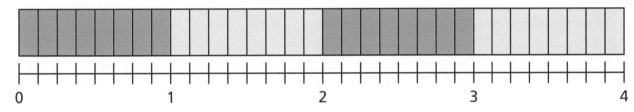

B

$1 =$ ☐ eighths

$3 =$ ☐ eighths

$3\frac{1}{8} =$ ☐ eighths $= \dfrac{☐}{8}$

Spot the mistake

$1\frac{4}{5} = \frac{8}{5}$

✔ Good to go?

Write these mixed numbers as improper fractions.

a) $3\frac{2}{5}$ **b)** $1\frac{2}{3}$ **c)** $2\frac{3}{8}$ **d)** $3\frac{1}{10}$

Convert from improper fractions to mixed numbers

➡️ **Starting point**

Display the number line in graphic **A** and the first row of questions. Ask:

● *What whole number is each of these fractions equal to: $\frac{5}{5}$, $\frac{10}{5}$, $\frac{15}{5}$, $\frac{20}{5}$?* [1, 2, 3, 4]

Reveal the second row of questions. Ask:

● *Who can point to $\frac{12}{5}$ on the number line? Between which two whole numbers is this?* [2 and 3] *How can we say $\frac{12}{5}$ as a mixed number?* [$2\frac{2}{5}$]

● *Between which two whole numbers is $\frac{19}{5}$?* [3 and 4]. *What is $\frac{19}{5}$ as a mixed number?* [$3\frac{4}{5}$]

● *What calculation can we do to find these mixed numbers?* Prompt the pupils to notice that they can divide the numerator of the improper fraction by 5 to give the whole number part of the mixed number and the remainder becomes the numerator; the denominator stays the same.

Repeat the activity for graphic **B**. After exploring the whole numbers, encourage the pupils to see that $\frac{11}{8}$ comes between 1 and 2 and is the mixed number $1\frac{3}{8}$ and that $\frac{21}{8}$ comes between 2 and 3 and is the mixed number $2\frac{5}{8}$.

Provide further improper fractions and challenge the pupils to convert them to mixed numbers, for example $\frac{7}{5}$, $\frac{81}{8}$, $\frac{25}{4}$, and $\frac{13}{3}$. [$1\frac{2}{5}$, $10\frac{1}{8}$, $6\frac{1}{4}$, $4\frac{1}{3}$] Each time, ask the pupils to describe their method of calculation.

> **Key point:** To write an improper fraction as a mixed number, divide the numerator by the denominator to get the whole number part of the mixed number. The remainder becomes the numerator and the denominator stays the same.

🔍 **Spot the mistake**

Ask:

● *The statement says '$\frac{17}{4} = 3\frac{5}{4}$'. Is this the answer you would have given?* [no] *Why not?* [The fraction of the mixed number is still an improper fraction.]

● *How could it be improved?* [by making one more whole]

● *What would be a better answer?* [$4\frac{1}{4}$]

✔️ **Good to go?**

Answers: a) $2\frac{1}{3}$ **b)** $4\frac{2}{5}$ **c)** $2\frac{5}{6}$ **d)** $4\frac{7}{10}$

Pupil book practice   Pages 10 and 11

As in the previous unit, some of the **Challenge** questions include tenths and hundredths that use the same digits for mixed numbers and their related improper fractions, for example $\frac{43}{10}$ = $4\frac{3}{10}$ or $\frac{223}{100}$ = $2\frac{23}{100}$. It is important for the pupils to realise that these are special cases and this pattern does not work for other fractions.

Starting point

A

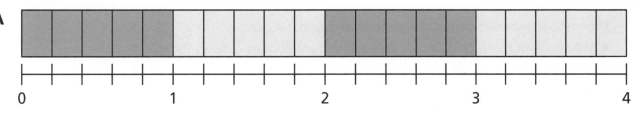

$\frac{5}{5} =$

$\frac{10}{5} =$

$\frac{15}{5} =$

$\frac{20}{5} =$

$\frac{12}{5} =$ $\frac{}{5}$

$\frac{19}{5} =$ $\frac{}{5}$

B

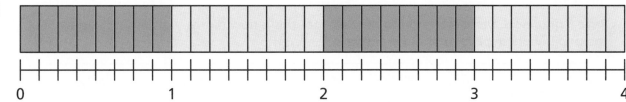

$\frac{8}{8} =$

$\frac{16}{8} =$

$\frac{24}{8} =$

$\frac{32}{8} =$

$\frac{11}{8} =$ $\frac{}{8}$

$\frac{21}{8} =$ $\frac{}{8}$

Spot the mistake

$$\frac{17}{4} = 3\frac{5}{4}$$

Good to go?

Write these improper fractions as mixed numbers.

a) $\frac{7}{3}$ b) $\frac{22}{5}$ c) $\frac{17}{6}$ d) $\frac{47}{10}$

Add or subtract fractions with the same denominator

→ Starting point

Show the number line and first question in graphic **A**. Ask:

- *What is $\frac{7}{10}$ plus $\frac{6}{10}$ plus $\frac{3}{10}$? How can we find out?* Count on along the number line together to find the answer. [$\frac{16}{10}$]
- *What do you notice about the numerator of the answer?* [It is the total of the three numerators in the question.]
- *What do you notice about the denominator of the answer?* [It is the same as those in the question and has not changed.]
- *How can we write $\frac{16}{10}$ in another way?* [$1\frac{6}{10}$]

Show the second question. Ask:

- *What is $\frac{11}{10}$ take away $\frac{2}{10}$?* [$\frac{9}{10}$] Draw attention again to the fact that the denominator of the answer is the same as the denominators in the question.

Show the third and fourth questions in graphic **A**. Jump on and back on the number line to demonstrate the addition and subtraction in the third question and help the pupils to find the answers. [$\frac{14}{10}$, $1\frac{4}{10}$] However, the pupils will have to work out the answer to the fourth question without the aid of a number line. [$\frac{30}{10}$, 3]

Reveal graphic **B**. Draw attention to the fact that this is now ninths, not tenths. Suggest that the pupils work in pairs to find the answers. [$\frac{7}{9}$, $\frac{11}{9}$, $1\frac{2}{9}$]

> **Key point:** For fractions with the same denominator, only the numerators are added or subtracted. The denominator of the answer is the same.

◯ Spot the mistake

Ask:

- *What is the mistake in this statement?* [The denominators have been added, which is incorrect.]
- *What should have been done?* [Only the numerators should have been added. The denominator should stay the same].
- *What should the answer be as an improper fraction?* [$\frac{9}{5}$]
- *What should the answer be as a mixed number?* [$1\frac{4}{5}$]

✔ Good to go?

Answers: a) $\frac{6}{7}$ **b)** $\frac{13}{8}$, $1\frac{5}{8}$ **c)** $\frac{5}{4}$, $1\frac{1}{4}$

> ## Pupil book practice   **Pages 12 and 13**
>
> This unit builds upon the previous two units by asking the pupils to give answers both as improper fractions and as mixed numbers. The later questions in this unit bring in equivalence and adding and subtracting measurements including units of time.

→ Starting point

A

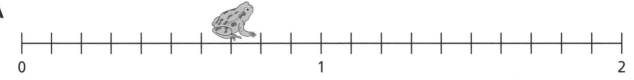

$$\frac{7}{10} + \frac{6}{10} + \frac{3}{10} = \frac{\square}{\square} = \square$$

$$\frac{11}{10} - \frac{2}{10} = \frac{\square}{\square}$$

$$\frac{8}{10} + \frac{8}{10} - \frac{2}{10} = \frac{\square}{\square} = \square$$

$$\frac{22}{10} - \frac{1}{10} + \frac{9}{10} = \frac{\square}{\square} = \square$$

B

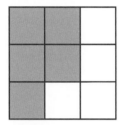

$$\frac{5}{9} + \frac{3}{9} - \frac{1}{9} = \frac{\square}{\square}$$

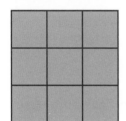 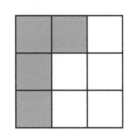

$$\frac{13}{9} - \frac{7}{9} + \frac{5}{9} = \frac{\square}{\square} = \square$$

🔍 Spot the mistake

$$\frac{3}{5} + \frac{4}{5} + \frac{2}{5} = \frac{9}{15}$$

✔ Good to go?

a) $\frac{10}{7} - \frac{4}{7} = \frac{\square}{\square}$

b) $\frac{3}{8} + \frac{6}{8} + \frac{4}{8} = \frac{\square}{\square} = \square$

c) $\frac{13}{4} + \frac{2}{4} - \frac{10}{4} = \frac{\square}{\square} = \square$

Add or subtract fractions with different denominators

➡️ **Starting point**

Show the question and number line in graphic **A**. Ask:

- *What is $\frac{3}{10}$ plus $\frac{1}{2}$? How can we find out?* Discuss the fact that it is difficult to add fractions that have different denominators.
- *Can we change one of the fractions so that they both have the same denominator? Which fraction could we change?* [$\frac{1}{2}$] *To what denominator?* [10] *How many tenths is $\frac{1}{2}$ equal to?* [$\frac{5}{10}$]

Reveal the next line in graphic **A**. Count along the number line to show that $\frac{3}{10}$ and $\frac{5}{10}$ have a total of $\frac{8}{10}$.

Show the question and number line in graphic **B**. Ask:

- *How can we add $\frac{1}{8}$ and $\frac{3}{4}$?* [Change one of the fractions so that the fractions have the same denominator.] Prompt the pupils to see that $\frac{3}{4}$ can be changed to the equivalent fraction $\frac{6}{8}$.

Reveal the next line in graphic **B** and show that the total is $\frac{7}{8}$ by counting on along the number line.

Show graphic **C**. Ask:

- *What is $\frac{3}{10}$ take away $\frac{27}{100}$?* Discuss how to change $\frac{3}{10}$ to $\frac{30}{100}$ so that the denominators are the same to reach the answer $\frac{3}{100}$.

> **Key point:** To add and subtract fractions with different denominators, change one or both of them to equivalent fractions so that they have the same denominator. Then only the numerators are added or subtracted and the denominator of the answer stays the same.

🔍 **Spot the mistake**

Ask:

- *What is the mistake in this statement?* [The numerators and denominators have both been added but this is not correct.]
- *What should have been done?* [One of the fractions should have been changed to an equivalent fraction so that the denominators were the same before adding.]
- *How many tenths are equivalent to $\frac{3}{5}$?* [$\frac{6}{10}$]
- *What should the answer be?* [$\frac{7}{10}$]

✔️ **Good to go?**

Answers: a) $\frac{5}{8}$ **b)** $\frac{3}{6}$ **c)** $\frac{9}{10}$

The pupils might give the answer $\frac{1}{2}$ for **b)**, which is also correct, though the pupils are not expected to simplify every answer at this stage.

> ## Pupil book practice   **Pages 14 and 15**
>
> Provide the pupils with fraction walls to help them find equivalent fractions if they find this difficult. Some of the later **Challenge** questions involve changing more than one of the fractions so that they all have the same denominator, while questions 25 and 26 require an understanding of how to write decimals with two decimal places as fractions with the denominator 100. Observe which pupils can confidently link this work to their understanding of decimals.

→ Starting point

A

$$\frac{3}{10} + \frac{1}{2} =$$

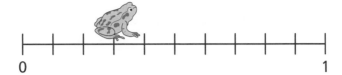

$$\frac{3}{10} + \boxed{\frac{1}{2}} = \qquad \frac{3}{10} + \boxed{\frac{5}{10}} = \frac{\boxed{}}{\boxed{}}$$

B

$$\frac{1}{8} + \frac{3}{4} =$$

$$\frac{1}{8} + \boxed{\frac{3}{4}} = \qquad \frac{1}{8} + \boxed{\frac{6}{8}} = \frac{\boxed{}}{\boxed{}}$$

C $\boxed{\frac{3}{10}} - \frac{27}{100} = \qquad \frac{\boxed{}}{100} - \frac{27}{100} = \frac{\boxed{}}{100}$

◯ Spot the mistake

$$\frac{3}{5} + \frac{1}{10} = \frac{4}{15}$$

✔ Good to go?

a) $\frac{3}{8} + \frac{1}{4} = \dfrac{\boxed{}}{\boxed{}}$ b) $\frac{5}{6} - \frac{1}{3} = \dfrac{\boxed{}}{\boxed{}}$ c) $\frac{1}{5} + \frac{7}{10} = \dfrac{\boxed{}}{\boxed{}}$

Compare fractions with different denominators

➡️ **Starting point**

Show the question and number line in graphic **A**. Ask:

- *How can we find out which fraction is larger: $\frac{3}{10}$ or $\frac{1}{2}$?* Explain that it is difficult to compare fractions that have different denominators. Suggest changing one of the fractions so that the denominators are the same.

- *Which fraction could we change?* [$\frac{1}{2}$] *To what denominator?* [10] *How many tenths is $\frac{1}{2}$ equal to?* [$\frac{5}{10}$]

Reveal the next line in graphic **A**. Ask:

- *Is it easier to compare them now?* [yes] *Which fraction is larger?* [$\frac{5}{10}$ or $\frac{1}{2}$ is larger than $\frac{3}{10}$.] Mark both fractions on the number line to allow the pupils to compare them.

Show the question and number line in graphic **B**. Ask:

- *How can we find out which fraction is larger: $\frac{5}{8}$ or $\frac{3}{4}$?* Reveal the rest of graphic **B** and encourage the pupils to see that $\frac{3}{4}$ can be changed to the equivalent fraction $\frac{6}{8}$ to make the fractions easier to compare.

- *Which is larger?* [$\frac{3}{4}$ is larger than $\frac{5}{8}$] This time encourage the pupils to give the original fraction rather than the converted fraction as the answer. Again, mark both fractions on the number line to enable the pupils to compare them.

Show graphic **C**. Ask:

- *Which is larger: $\frac{7}{10}$ or $\frac{69}{100}$?* Explain how to first change $\frac{7}{10}$ to $\frac{70}{100}$ so that the denominators are the same and then to compare $\frac{70}{100}$ and $\frac{69}{100}$ to see which of the original fractions is larger. [$\frac{7}{10}$]

> **Key point:** To make it easier to compare fractions, change one or both of them to equivalent fractions so that they have the same denominator.

🔍 **Spot the mistake**

Ask:

- *How can we find out if $\frac{4}{5}$ is smaller than $\frac{7}{10}$?* [It is easier to compare tenths with tenths, so $\frac{4}{5}$ can be changed to the equivalent fraction $\frac{8}{10}$.]

- *Is $\frac{4}{5}$ smaller or larger than $\frac{7}{10}$?* [It is larger, as $\frac{8}{10}$ is larger than $\frac{7}{10}$.]

✔️ **Good to go?**

Answers: a) $\frac{3}{8}$ **b)** $\frac{5}{6}$ **c)** $\frac{3}{4}$

Pupil book practice   Pages 18 and 19

As these ideas are similar to those in the previous unit, some pupils will be more confident in changing fractions to equivalents to make answering the questions easier. If necessary, provide the pupils with fraction walls to help them find equivalent fractions. Revise the < or > signs if any pupils show confusion with this. Some of the later **Challenge** questions involve changing more than one of the fractions so that they all have the same denominator. Suggest a denominator if the pupils are unsure, for example in question 28 all the fractions can be changed to have the denominator 30.

Starting point

A Which is larger: $\frac{3}{10}$ or $\frac{1}{2}$?

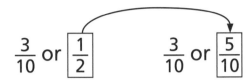

$\frac{3}{10}$ or $\boxed{\frac{1}{2}}$ $\frac{3}{10}$ or $\boxed{\frac{5}{10}}$

B Which is larger: $\frac{5}{8}$ or $\frac{3}{4}$?

$\frac{5}{8}$ or $\boxed{\frac{3}{4}}$ $\frac{5}{8}$ or $\boxed{\frac{6}{8}}$

C Which is larger: $\frac{7}{10}$ or $\frac{69}{100}$?

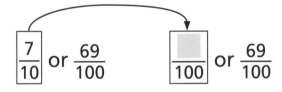

$\boxed{\frac{7}{10}}$ or $\frac{69}{100}$ $\boxed{\dfrac{}{100}}$ or $\frac{69}{100}$

Spot the mistake

$\frac{4}{5}$ is smaller than $\frac{7}{10}$.

Good to go?

Which is larger?

a) $\frac{3}{8}$ or $\frac{1}{4}$ **b)** $\frac{5}{6}$ or $\frac{2}{3}$ **c)** $\frac{7}{12}$ or $\frac{3}{4}$

Find fractions of numbers and quantities

➡️ **Starting point**

Show the first two rows in graphic **A**. Ask:

- *How can we find $\frac{3}{8}$ of £32?* [Divide £32 by 8 to find $\frac{1}{8}$ and then multiply by 3 to find $\frac{3}{8}$.]
- *Which number do we divide?* [the quantity, £32]
- *Which number do we divide by?* [the denominator, 8]
- *Which number do we multiply by?* [the numerator, 3]
- *What is $\frac{1}{8}$ of £32?* [£4]

Show the row of 8 lots of £4 making the total of £32.

- *So what is $\frac{3}{8}$ of £32?* [£4 multiplied by 3 = £12]

Reveal graphic **B** and revise finding fractions by dividing by the denominator and then multiplying by the numerator. Remind the pupils to notice the first letters of the key words in this rule. Explain that you are also going to demonstrate another way of finding the answer to this type of question.

Reveal graphic **C**. Explain that you can also answer this question using equivalent fractions.

- *How can we find the missing number?* Show that 8 can be multiplied by 4 to give 32 so we can also multiply 3 by 4 to give the missing number 12.
- *What do you notice about the missing numerator?* [It is the answer to the question 'What is $\frac{3}{8}$ of £32?'] Point out that you write the quantity as the denominator and that the missing numerator will be the answer.

> **Key point:** To find a fraction of a quantity, divide by the denominator (to find one part) and multiply by the numerator (to find several parts). An alternative method is to use equivalent fractions.

🔍 **Spot the mistake**

Ask:

- *The statement says '$\frac{4}{5}$ of 40 = 24'. Is the answer 24 correct?* [no]
- *What could you do to work out the correct answer?* Discuss the two ways of finding the correct answer as outlined above and ask the pupils which method they prefer.
- *What is the correct answer?* [32]

✓ **Good to go?**

Answers: **a)** 24p **b)** £27 **c)** 35m

> ## Pupil book practice
> **Pages 20 and 21**
>
> This practice focuses on finding fractions of numbers and measures. Encourage the pupils to try to find answers using both the methods outlined above and to express their preference for how they like to answer the questions. Observe which pupils take time to find answers and note whether the reason for this is that they still need to learn all their tables and related division facts. If necessary, some pupils can be provided with a list of tables or a multiplication square so that their focus is on the methods rather than on the facts.

→ Starting point

A

£32

What is $\frac{3}{8}$ of £32?   £32 ÷ 8 × 3 = £

| £4 | £4 | £4 | £4 | £4 | £4 | £4 | £4 |

B Divide by the **d**enominator (to find one part) and **m**ultiply by the **n**umerator (to find several parts).

$\frac{\text{numerator}}{\text{denominator}}$ $\frac{3}{8}$ of £32 = £12

C What is $\frac{3}{8}$ of £32? $\frac{3}{8}$ = $\boxed{}$ £32

× £

× £

✎ Spot the mistake

$\frac{4}{5}$ of 40 = 24

✓ Good to go?

a) Find $\frac{2}{3}$ of 36p.   **b)** Find $\frac{3}{4}$ of £36.   **c)** Find $\frac{7}{100}$ of 500m.

Multiply fractions by whole numbers

➡️ Starting point

Show graphic **A**. Ask:

- *What is $\frac{3}{10}$ multiplied by 3? How can we find out?* Use the number line to show the pupils that 3 lots of $\frac{3}{10}$ is $\frac{9}{10}$.
- *What do you notice about the denominator of the answer?* [It is the same as the denominator in the question.] Discuss that, in the same way that multiplying 3 lemons by 3 gives 9 lemons, multiplying 3 tenths by 3 gives 9 tenths. The 10, the denominator, does not get multiplied.

Show graphic **B**. Ask:

- *Which part of the fraction do we multiply to find the answer to this question?* [only the numerator]
- *What is $\frac{5}{8}$ multiplied by 3?* [$\frac{15}{8}$] Encourage the pupils to give the answer as an improper fraction first, pointing out that the denominator is still eighths.
- *Can you use the number line to convert $\frac{15}{8}$ to a mixed number?* [$1\frac{7}{8}$] If necessary, revise the ideas in Unit 4 to remind the pupils how to change an improper fraction into a mixed number.

Reveal graphic **C**. Ask:

- *What is $\frac{4}{9}$ multiplied by 5 as an improper fraction?* [$\frac{20}{9}$] *What is it as a mixed number?* [$2\frac{2}{9}$]
- *How many sixths is $\frac{5}{6}$ multiplied by 12?* [$\frac{60}{6}$] Prompt the pupils to realise that $\frac{60}{6}$ is the whole number 10.

> **Key point:** When multiplying a fraction by a whole number, multiply only the numerator. The denominator stays the same.

🔍 Spot the mistake

Ask:

- *The statement says '$\frac{3}{4} \times 3 = \frac{9}{12}$'. Is this true?* [no]
- *What is the mistake?* [The denominator has been multiplied too.]
- *What is the correct answer?* [$\frac{9}{4}$ or $2\frac{1}{4}$]

✓ Good to go?

Answers: a) $\frac{6}{7}$ **b)** $\frac{16}{5}$, $3\frac{1}{5}$ **c)** $\frac{40}{10}$, 4   **d)** $\frac{27}{100}$

Pupil book practice   Pages 22 and 23

The early questions in this unit provide visual assistance in finding answers. Nevertheless, encourage the pupils to check their answers by looking at the numerators and denominators and ensuring that only the numerators are multiplied by the whole number. The **Challenge** questions involve hundredths in preparation for work in later units on decimals and percentages. If necessary, for those pupils without a solid knowledge of all their times tables, provide a multiplication square so that their focus is on the method rather than on the multiplication facts.

→ Starting point

A $\frac{3}{10} \times 3 = \dfrac{}{}$

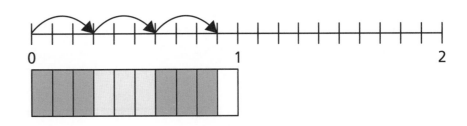

B $\frac{5}{8} \times 3 = \dfrac{}{} = \square$

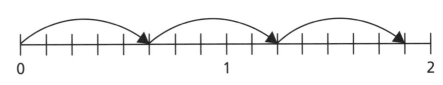

C $\frac{4}{9} \times 5 = \dfrac{}{} = \square$ $\frac{5}{6} \times 12 = \dfrac{}{} = \square$

🔍 Spot the mistake

$$\frac{3}{4} \times 3 = \frac{9}{12}$$

✔ Good to go?

a) $\frac{3}{7} \times 2 \;\; = \dfrac{}{}$

b) $\frac{4}{5} \times 4 \;\; = \dfrac{}{} = \square$

c) $\frac{5}{10} \times 8 \;\; = \dfrac{}{} = \square$

d) $\frac{9}{100} \times 3 \;\; = \dfrac{}{}$

Multiply fractions and mixed numbers by whole numbers

➡️ **Starting point**

Display the first line of graphic **A** and revise the work from the previous unit on multiplying fractions by whole numbers. Ask:

● *Which part of the fraction do we multiply to find the answer to this question?* [only the numerator]

Reveal the second line of graphic **A**.

● *What is $\frac{2}{3}$ multiplied by 5?* [$\frac{10}{3}$] Encourage the pupils to give the answer as an improper fraction first, pointing out that the denominator is still thirds.

● *What is $\frac{10}{3}$ as a mixed number?* [$3\frac{1}{3}$] Use the cake visuals as an aid.

Show the first line of graphic **B**. Ask:

● *How do we multiply $2\frac{2}{3}$ by 5?* Explain that the whole number part and the fraction part should be treated separately, multiplying each by 5 and then adding the answers together.

Reveal the rest of graphic **B** and talk through the notation.

● *2 wholes times 5 is how many wholes?* [10]. *What was the answer to $\frac{2}{3}$ times 5?* [$3\frac{1}{3}$] Show how the two can be added to find the answer. [$10 + 3\frac{1}{3} = 13\frac{1}{3}$].

Work through the examples in graphics **C** and **D** in the same way:

● $3\frac{4}{9} \times 2 = (3 \times 2) + (\frac{4}{9} \times 2) = 6 + \frac{8}{9} = 6\frac{8}{9}$

● $4\frac{5}{7} \times 3 = (4 \times 3) + (\frac{5}{7} \times 3) = 12 + \frac{15}{7} = 12 + 2\frac{1}{7} = 14\frac{1}{7}$

> **Key point:** When multiplying a mixed number by a whole number, treat the whole number part and the fraction part of the mixed number separately. Multiply each of these by the whole number and then add the answers together.

🔍 **Spot the mistake**

Ask:

● *The statement says '$2\frac{3}{4} \times 3 = 6\frac{9}{4}$'. What is the mistake?* [The fraction part of the answer is an improper fraction. It should be changed.]

● *What should we do to work out this answer correctly?* [The improper fraction in the answer should be changed: $(2 \times 3) + (\frac{3}{4} \times 3) = 6 + \frac{9}{4} = 6 + 2\frac{1}{4} = 8\frac{1}{4}$]

✓ **Good to go?**

Answers: a) $10\frac{6}{7}$ **b)** $5\frac{2}{5}$ **c)** $8\frac{5}{10}$

The pupils might give the answer $8\frac{1}{2}$ for **c)**, which is also correct.

> ## Pupil book practice   **Pages 24 and 25**
>
> The early questions in this unit provide further practice of multiplying proper fractions, as taught in the previous unit, because this skill must be mastered before multiplying mixed numbers can take place. The questions then go on to include mixed numbers.

→ Starting point

A

$\frac{2}{3} \times 5$

$\frac{2}{3} \times 5 = \frac{10}{3} = \boxed{}$

B

$2\frac{2}{3} \times 5$

$2\frac{2}{3} \times 5 = (2 \times 5) \; + \; (\frac{2}{3} \times 5)$

$\qquad\qquad = \quad 10 \quad + \quad 3\frac{1}{3} \quad = \boxed{}$

C $3\frac{4}{9} \times 2 = (3 \times 2) + (\frac{4}{9} \times 2) = \boxed{} + \dfrac{\boxed{}}{\boxed{}} = \boxed{}$

D $4\frac{5}{7} \times 3 = (4 \times 3) + (\frac{5}{7} \times 3) = \boxed{} + \boxed{} = \boxed{}$

○ Spot the mistake

$2\frac{3}{4} \times 3 = 6\frac{9}{4}$

✔ Good to go?

a) $5\frac{3}{7} \times 2 = \boxed{}$ **b)** $1\frac{4}{5} \times 3 = \boxed{}$ **c)** $1\frac{7}{10} \times 5 = \boxed{}$

Round decimals to the nearest whole number and tenth

 Starting point

Show the ruler in graphic **A**. Ask:

- *There are two lines above the ruler. How long is the top line?* [1.7cm]
- *About how long is the bottom line?* [Prompt for responses between 2.4cm and 2.5cm.]
- *Can anyone tell me a decimal that lies between 2.4 and 2.5?* [2.41, 2.42, and so on] Revise how the interval can be split into 10 parts. Tell the pupils that the bottom line is 2.43cm.

Reveal the grids below the ruler. Explain that the column headings are abbreviations for ones, tenths and hundredths.

Show the first two rows in graphic **B**. Ask:

- *Which two whole numbers does 1.7 lie between?* [1 and 2]
- *Which whole number is 1.7 nearest to?* [2] Explain that 1.7 when rounded to the nearest whole number is 2. Repeat for 2.43, prompting the pupils to recognise that it is closer to the whole number 2 than to 3.

Tell the pupils that the tenths digit can show you which whole number to round to. If the tenths digit is 5 or more, round up to the next whole number. If not, round down.

Show the next row in graphic **B**. Explain that this decimal can also be rounded to the nearest tenth (which is sometimes also called 'to one decimal place'). The answer will have a tenths digit. Ask:

- *What is 2.43 to the nearest tenth? Is it 2.4 or 2.5?* [2.4] Demonstrate that looking at the hundredths digit can help to you work it out. If it is 5 or more, round up. If not, round down.

> **Key point:** To round to the nearest whole number, look at the tenths digit. If it is 5 or more, round up. If not, round down. To round to the nearest tenth (to one decimal place), look at the hundredths digit. If it is 5 or more, round up. If not, round down.

 Spot the mistake

Ask:

- *The statement says '3.52 rounded to the nearest tenth is 3.6'. Is this true?* [no]
- *Why isn't it true?* [The hundredths digit is less than 5 so round down to 3.5.]

 Good to go?

Answers: a) 8   **b)** 8.5   **c)** 1   **d)** 3.1

> ## Pupil book practice   **Pages 26 and 27**
>
> Some pupils find rounding quite difficult at first. They may therefore benefit from being given number lines showing tenths and hundredths in order to see which whole numbers or which tenths lie either side of the decimal given (available to download from the Schofield & Sims website). Even if they are using number lines, encourage the pupils to gradually see patterns in the digits in the questions and answers. This will help them to move towards working out answers mentally without these aids.

→ Starting point

A

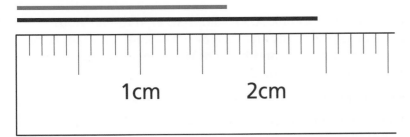

1cm   2cm

O	.	t	h
1	.	7	

O	.	t	h
2	.	4	3

B Nearest whole number?   1   1.7   2
                                        ↑

                              2   2.43   3
                                        ↑

Nearest tenth?   2.4   2.43   2.5
                                        ↑

⊙ Spot the mistake

3.52 rounded to the nearest tenth is 3.6.

✓ Good to go?

a) Round 8.4 to the nearest whole number.

b) Round 8.45 to the nearest tenth.

c) Round 1.14 to the nearest whole number.

d) Round 3.07 to the nearest tenth.

Understand thousandths as fractions and decimals

→ Starting point

Show just the column headings of the grid in graphic **A**. Explain that, as in the previous lesson, they are abbreviations. Discuss that the digits after the decimal point stand for parts of a whole. These are tenths, hundredths and thousandths, with tenths being larger than hundredths and hundredths being larger than thousandths.

Reveal the decimals in the grid one by one. Ask:

● *How do we say this decimal?* [zero point seven] *What does it stand for?* [7 tenths] *How can we write it as a fraction?* [$\frac{7}{10}$]

● *How do we say this next decimal?* [zero point zero three] *What does it stand for?* [3 hundredths] *How can we write it as a fraction?* [$\frac{3}{100}$]

● *How do we say this next decimal?* [zero point five one] *What does it stand for?* [5 tenths and 1 hundredth] *How can we write it as a fraction?* [$\frac{51}{100}$]

● *How do we say this next decimal?* [zero point zero eight six] *What does it stand for?* [86 thousandths]

● *How do we say this final decimal?* [zero point one two five] *What does it stand for?* [125 thousandths]

Show graphic **B**. Invite the pupils to come to the front to write each fraction as a decimal. List these under the correct place value column headings and try to get all of the pupils to agree on them. [0.9, 0.07, 0.12, 0.003, 0.016, 0.255]

> **Key point:** The columns to the right of the decimal point stand for tenths, hundredths, thousandths and so on. The position of the last digit (higher than 0) in the decimal indicates whether they are tenths, hundredths or thousandths.

○ Spot the mistake

Ask:

● *The statement says '$\frac{12}{1000}$ = 0.12'. Is this true?* [no]

● *Why isn't it true?* [0.12 is 12 hundredths not 12 thousandths.]

● *How can we write $\frac{12}{1000}$ correctly as a decimal?* [0.012]

✓ Good to go?

Answers: a) $\frac{4}{1000}$ **b)** $\frac{4}{100}$ **c)** $\frac{13}{1000}$ **d)** $\frac{539}{1000}$

> ## Pupil book practice   **Pages 28 and 29**
>
> If the pupils are confident with tenths and hundredths, they usually move on to thousandths without much difficulty. However, those pupils who are not confident with simple decimals may benefit from revision of tenths and hundredths first, perhaps revisiting Units 13 and 14 from **Fractions 4**. The **Get started** section of this unit revises these ideas before moving on to thousandths in the later sections. The final questions include links to equivalence work to help the pupils appreciate that fractions with denominators that are not 10, 100 or 1000 can also be written as decimals.

→ Starting point

A

O	.	t	h	th
0	.	7		
0	.	0	3	
0	.	5	1	
0	.	0	8	6
0	.	1	2	5

B How do you write:

$\frac{9}{10}$ as a decimal? $\frac{7}{100}$ as a decimal?

$\frac{12}{100}$ as a decimal? $\frac{3}{1000}$ as a decimal?

$\frac{16}{1000}$ as a decimal? $\frac{255}{1000}$ as a decimal?

 Spot the mistake

$\frac{12}{1000} = 0.12$

 Good to go?

Write each decimal as a fraction.

a) 0.004   **b)** 0.04   **c)** 0.013   **d)** 0.539

Compare decimals with up to three decimal places

➡️ **Starting point**

Before showing any graphics, ask:

● *Which is larger: 1 tenth or 1 hundredth?* [1 tenth]
● *Which is larger: 1 hundredth or 1 thousandth?* [1 hundredth]

Show the column headings in graphic **A**. Explain that the value of the columns gets 10 times smaller as you move across to the right, so ones are 10 times larger than tenths, tenths are 10 times larger than hundredths and hundredths are 10 times larger than thousandths.

Show the first two decimals in the grid on graphic **A**. Ask:

● *How can we find out which is larger: 0.4 or 0.37?* Many pupils will think that 0.37 is larger than 0.4 as 37 is larger than 4, but remind them (for decimals less than 1) to always start by comparing the tenths digits.
● *Is 4 tenths larger than 3 tenths?* [yes] *So which is larger: 0.4 or 0.37?* [0.4] Remind the pupils that 0.4 is equal to 0.40, which is 40 hundredths. If you write the zero on the end of the decimal it is easier to see that 0.40 is larger than 0.37. Remind the pupils that writing a zero on the end of a decimal does not change its value.

Show the next two decimals in the grid on graphic **A**. Ask:

● *How can we find out which is larger: 0.096 or 0.145?* [Compare the tenths.]
● *Is 0 tenths or 1 tenth larger?* [1 tenth] *So which is larger: 0.096 or 0.145?* [0.145]

Display graphic **B**. First revise the greater than and less than signs (< >). Ask:

● *Which sign should we put between 0.4 and 0.37?* [>]
● *What about between 0.096 and 0.145?* [<]

Discuss the next two questions, showing how to compare tenths and then, if they are the same, to move across to hundredths to compare and so on. [0.201 > 0.07, 0.94 > 0.913] Remind the pupils to always work from the left when comparing decimals.

> **Key point:** When comparing decimals, compare each digit from the left. For decimals less than one, compare tenths first, then hundredths and then thousandths.

🔍 **Spot the mistake**

Ask:

● *The statement says that 0.6 is less than 0.54. Is this true?* [no]
● *How do you know?* [0.6 has 6 tenths and 0.54 has only 5 tenths, so 0.6 must be larger.]
● *How could we write 0.6 to make it easier to compare with 0.54?* [0.60]
● *Which sign should the statement use?* [>]

✓ **Good to go?**

Answers: a) 0.007, 0.07, 0.7 **b)** 0.031, 0.3, 0.31 **c)** 0.4, 0.47, 0.474 **d)** 0.101, 0.13, 0.97

> ## Pupil book practice   **Pages 32 and 33**
> This unit provides a wide range of practice in comparing and ordering decimals involving thousandths. Remind the pupils that they can write a zero on the end of decimals so that they have the same number of decimal places in order to make them easier to compare. Some of the questions involve measurements such as centimetres, metres, kilograms and money.

Starting point

A

O	.	t	h	th
0	.	4		
0	.	3	7	
0	.	0	9	6
0	.	1	4	5

B Show which is larger using the < or > sign.

0.4 0.37   0.096 0.145

0.201 0.07   0.94 0.913

 Spot the mistake

0.6 < 0.54

✓ **Good to go?**

Order these decimals from smallest to largest.

a) 0.007, 0.7, 0.07   **b)** 0.31, 0.031, 0.3

c) 0.474, 0.47, 0.4   **d)** 0.101, 0.97, 0.13

Solve problems with decimals up to three decimal places

➡ Starting point

Show the question in graphic **A** without showing the grid beneath it. Ask:

- *How could we find out the total of these two decimals?* Tell the pupils that it is vital to add tenths to tenths, hundredths to hundredths and so on and that it helps to write the decimals in the correct columns so that the decimal points line up. Reveal the question written out in columns and talk the pupils through adding each column.
- *What is the answer to 0.4 + 0.37?* [0.77]

Show the question in graphic **B** without showing the grid beneath it. Ask:

- *How can we subtract 0.047 from 0.7 in a similar way?* Discuss how a written method can be used, provided that zeros are written on the end of one of the decimals so that both have the same number of decimal places.
- *Which decimal should we add zeros to?* [0.7] *How many zeros should we add?* [2] Reveal the question written out in columns and talk the pupils through the subtraction calculation.
- *What is the answer to 0.7 − 0.047?* [0.653]

Practise with a few more simple examples containing tenths that could be done mentally, for example 0.5 + 0.4 = 0.9, 1.7 − 0.3 = 1.4, 0.8 + 0.8 = 1.6 and so on. Write them out in columns if the pupils give incorrect answers.

> **Key point:** Decimals can be added and subtracted in the same way as whole numbers, provided that the decimals are aligned correctly with the decimal points under each other.

🔍 Spot the mistake

Ask:

- *Is 0.5 plus 0.6 equal to 0.11?* [no]
- *What is the mistake?* [The 5 tenths and 6 tenths should be added to make 11 tenths but the answer shows 11 hundredths not 11 tenths.]
- *What is the correct answer?* [5 tenths + 6 tenths = 11 tenths which is 1 whole and 1 tenth or 1.1]

✔ Good to go?

Answers: a) 1.4   **b)** 0.556   **c)** 0.175   **d)** 0.234

> ## Pupil book practice   Pages 34 and 35
>
> This unit provides opportunities for the pupils to solve problems that involve adding and subtracting decimals and reasoning about tenths and hundredths. Question 27 includes negative decimals which can be introduced if the pupils are familiar with negative whole numbers. Encourage the pupils to see that you can count forwards or backwards from zero in decimal steps creating sequences such as 0.4, 0.2, 0, −0.2, −0.4, −0.6 and so on.

→ Starting point

A $0.4 + 0.37 =$ ☐

O	.	t	h	th
0	.	4		
+ 0	.	3	7	
= 0	.	7	7	

B $0.7 - 0.047 =$ ☐

O	.	t	h	th
0	.	$\not{7}^6$	$\not{0}^9$	$^1 0$
− 0	.	0	4	7
= 0	.	6	5	3

🔍 Spot the mistake

$0.5 + 0.6 = 0.11$

✔ Good to go?

a) $0.9 + 0.5 =$ ☐　　　　　**b)** $0.4 + 0.156 =$ ☐

c) $0.425 - 0.25 =$ ☐　　　　**d)** $0.6 - 0.366 =$ ☐

Understand percentages as fractions

➡️ Starting point

Show graphic **A**. Ask:

- *Does anyone know what this symbol stands for?* Tell the pupils that the symbol is called the percentage symbol and that 'per cent' means 'per hundred' or 'out of 100' or 'for every 100'. Explain that percentages are just a different way of describing fractions or decimals.

Reveal each row of graphic **B** in turn. For each one, ask:

- *How can this percentage be written as a fraction?* [1% = $\frac{1}{100}$, 14% = $\frac{14}{100}$ and 40% = $\frac{40}{100}$]

Focus on the last row of graphic **B**. Ask:

- *Could we write $\frac{40}{100}$ in a different way, as an equivalent fraction?* [$\frac{40}{100} = \frac{4}{10} = \frac{2}{5}$] Explain that all of these equivalent fractions are equal to the percentage 40%.

Reveal graphic **C**. Challenge the pupils to write each percentage as a fraction and to simplify them where possible. [$\frac{7}{100}$, $\frac{99}{100}$, $\frac{30}{100} = \frac{3}{10}$, $\frac{50}{100} = \frac{5}{10} = \frac{1}{2}$, $\frac{80}{100} = \frac{8}{10} = \frac{4}{5}$, $\frac{25}{100} = \frac{1}{4}$]

> **Key point:** The percentage symbol '%' stands for 'out of every 100', so 27% means '27 out of 100' or $\frac{27}{100}$ or 27 hundredths.

🔍 Spot the mistake

Ask:

- *Is 9% equal to $\frac{9}{10}$?* [no]
- *Why not?* [9% stands for 9 out of every 100 or 9 hundredths, not 9 tenths.]
- *What is the correct equivalent fraction?* [$\frac{9}{100}$]

✔️ Good to go?

Answers: a) $\frac{37}{100}$ **b)** $\frac{91}{100}$ **c)** $\frac{20}{100} = \frac{2}{10} = \frac{1}{5}$ **d)** $\frac{75}{100} = \frac{3}{4}$

Pupil book practice   Pages 36 and 37

This unit provides a wide range of practice in converting between percentages and fractions and vice versa, making links to the common equivalent fractions later in the unit. Later questions also involve a greater appreciation of sets of percentages totalling 100% (the whole) and beginning to describe pence or centimetres as percentages of a pound or metre respectively. Some pupils may benefit from being given a comparison chart showing fractions, percentages and decimals (available to download from the Schofield & Sims website).

➡️ Starting point

A   **%** (per cent)

B

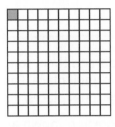
1%   1 hundredth $\frac{1}{100}$

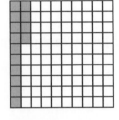
14%   14 hundredths $\frac{14}{100}$

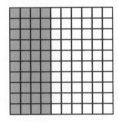
40%   40 hundredths $\frac{40}{100}$

C How do you write:

7% as a fraction?   99% as a fraction?

30% as a fraction?   50% as a fraction?

80% as a fraction?   25% as a fraction?

🔍 Spot the mistake

9% = $\frac{9}{10}$

✔️ Good to go?

Write each percentage as a fraction.

a) 37%   **b)** 91%   **c)** 20%   **d)** 75%

Understand percentages as fractions and as decimals

→ **Starting point**

Begin by displaying graphic **A**. Ask:

- *If 50 of the 100 squares (50 hundredths) in this grid were shaded, how could we describe this as a percentage?* [50%]
- *What about as a fraction?* $[\frac{50}{100} = \frac{5}{10} = \frac{1}{2}]$
- *What about as a decimal?* [0.5]

Now invite the pupils to find percentages on the number line. Encourage them to notice that each 10% is 1 tenth, so can be written as a decimal with one decimal place. For example, 30% can be written as 0.3, rather than as 0.30 with two decimal places.

Reveal each row of graphic **B** in turn. For each row, discuss the proportion shown as a percentage, a decimal and a fraction.

- *What are the missing numbers for 43 hundredths?* [43%, 0.43]
- *What are the missing numbers for 25 hundredths?* $[25\%, 0.25, \frac{25}{100}]$ *How can we simplify the fraction $\frac{25}{100}$?* $[\frac{1}{4}]$

Reveal graphic **C** and ask:

- *What is the decimal 0.1 (1 tenth) as a percentage?* Suggest that the pupils write a zero on the end of decimals with one decimal place to make the conversion to a percentage easier. In this instance, write 0.1 as 0.10 to find the answer. [10%]
- *What are the other missing numbers for 0.1?* $[10 \text{ hundredths}, \frac{10}{100}, \frac{1}{10}]$
- *What are the missing numbers for 0.9?* $[90 \text{ hundredths}, 90\%, \frac{90}{100}, \frac{9}{10}]$

> **Key point:** Proportions of a whole can be written as percentages, as decimals and as fractions, for example 17% = 0.17 = $\frac{17}{100}$. For decimals with one decimal place it can help to write a zero on the end to convert them to percentages, for example, 0.3 is 0.30 which is 30%.

🔍 **Spot the mistake**

Ask:

- *The statement says that 7% is equal to the decimal 0.7. Is this true?* [no]
- *Why isn't it true?* [7% is 7 hundredths which is 0.07.]
- *What percentage is equal to the decimal 0.7?* [0.7 or 0.70 is equal to 70%.]

✓ **Good to go?**

Answers: **a)** $0.04 = \frac{4}{100}$ or $\frac{1}{25}$　**b)** $0.91 = \frac{91}{100}$　**c)** $0.2 = \frac{20}{100}$ or $\frac{1}{5}$　**d)** $0.75 = \frac{75}{100}$ or $\frac{3}{4}$

> ## Pupil book practice　　　　　　　　　　　　　　**Pages 38 and 39**
>
> Some pupils may benefit from being given a fractions, decimals and percentages conversion sheet (available to download from the Schofield & Sims website) to help them with this work. Some questions in the **Now try these** section involve describing amounts such as £0.15 or 0.34m as percentages of a pound or metre respectively, as a practical application for converting between decimals and percentages.

Starting point

A

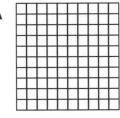

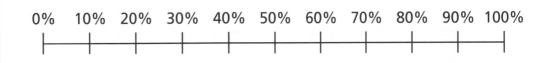

0%   10%   20%   30%   40%   50%   60%   70%   80%   90%   100%

B

	percentage	decimal	fraction
1 hundredth	1%	0.01	$\frac{1}{100}$
43 hundredths			$\frac{43}{100}$
25 hundredths			$\frac{}{100} = \frac{}{}$

C

	percentage	decimal	fraction
30 hundredths	30%	0.3	$\frac{30}{100} = \frac{3}{10}$
___ hundredths		0.1	$\frac{}{100} = \frac{}{10}$
___ hundredths		0.9	$\frac{}{100} = \frac{}{10}$

 Spot the mistake

7% = 0.7

✔ **Good to go?**

Write each as a decimal and as a fraction.

a) 4%   **b)** 91%   **c)** 20%   **d)** 75%

Relate percentages to 'finding fractions of'

→ Starting point

This unit builds on ideas from Unit 8 about finding fractions of numbers and quantities. As the pupils develop their understanding of the link between fractions and percentages, they can begin to find percentages of numbers and quantities in the same way.

Using graphic **A**, first show '50% of £32'. Ask:

- *How can we find 50% of a number? What fraction is 50% equivalent to?* [50% = $\frac{50}{100}$ = $\frac{1}{2}$]
  Explain that 50% of £32 is the same as $\frac{1}{2}$ of £32, which is £16. Show the rest of graphic **A** and explain that 50% is found by dividing an amount by 2.

Using graphic **B**, show '25% of £32'. Ask:

- *How can we find 25% of a number? What fraction is 25% equivalent to?* [25% = $\frac{25}{100}$ = $\frac{1}{4}$]
  Explain that 25% of £32 is the same as $\frac{1}{4}$ of £32, which is £8. Show the rest of graphic **B** and explain that 25% is found by dividing an amount by 4.

Using graphic **C**, show '10% of £40'. Ask:

- *How can we find 10% of a number? What fraction is 10% equivalent to?* [10% = $\frac{10}{100}$ = $\frac{1}{10}$]
  Explain that 10% of £40 is the same as $\frac{1}{10}$ of £40, which is £4. Show the rest of graphic **C** and explain that 10% is found by dividing an amount by 10.

Using graphic **D**, discuss how 1% is equivalent to $\frac{1}{100}$. Show that 1% of a number is found by dividing by 100. [1% of £200 = 200 ÷ 100 = 2]

> **Key point:** To find a percentage of a quantity, remember what fraction the percentage is equivalent to and find that fraction of the number. 50% = $\frac{1}{2}$ so divide by 2, 25% = $\frac{1}{4}$ so divide by 4, 10% = $\frac{1}{10}$ so divide by 10 and 1% = $\frac{1}{100}$ so divide by 100.

⌕ Spot the mistake

Ask:

- *The statement says '1% of 700m = 70m'. Is this true?* [no]
- *What is the mistake?* [70m is 10% of 700m, not 1%.]
- *What is the correct answer?* [1% is equivalent to 1 hundredth, so to find 1% of 700m we divide 700m by 100, which gives the answer 7m.]
- *What similar question could have the answer 70m?* [10% of 700m]

✓ Good to go?

Answers: a) 6cm   **b)** 5kg   **c)** 18mm   **d)** £12

Pupil book practice   Pages 40 and 41

These questions focus on finding simple percentages of numbers and measures. The early sections involve converting to unit fractions, as outlined above. As the pupils become more confident with this, they should begin to realise that these facts can be used to help them find other facts, for example if you know 10% you can double to find 20% or multiply by 8 to find 80% and so on. Question 26 also involves combining several known facts to find others by adding 50%, 25%, 10% and 1% to find 86%.

➡️ Starting point

A 50% of £32 $= \frac{1}{2}$ of £32   Divide by 2.

£32

£16	£16

B 25% of £32 $= \frac{1}{4}$ of £32   Divide by 4.

£32

£8	£8	£8	£8

C 10% of £40 $= \frac{1}{10}$ of £40   Divide by 10.

£40

£4	£4	£4	£4	£4	£4	£4	£4	£4	£4

D 1% of £200 $= \frac{1}{100}$ of £200   Divide by 100.

🔍 Spot the mistake

1% of 700m = 70m

✔️ Good to go?

a) Find 50% of 12cm.　　　　**b)** Find 25% of 20kg.

c) Find 10% of 180mm.　　　　**d)** Find 1% of £1200.

Solve fraction, decimal and percentage problems

➡️ Starting point

This unit draws together many of the ideas contained in this book and, as such, you may choose to focus on one aspect that you know the pupils have been finding more difficult than another. If this is not the case, then revise all aspects as follows.

Show the **Starting point** graphic and discuss the equivalence between percentages, decimals and fractions by inviting the pupils to identify equivalents and point to them on the number lines. Revise ideas from other units of this book by asking questions such as:

- *If a problem mentions 25%, what fraction or decimal would you think of?* $[\frac{25}{100}, \frac{1}{4}$ or 0.25]
- *How could you find $\frac{3}{4}$ of a length such as 36m?* [Divide by the denominator 4 and multiply by 3 to give the answer 27.]
- *How could you find 1% of a number?* $[1\% = \frac{1}{100}$, so divide the number by 100.]
- *For a problem that involves finding the total of two decimals, what should you remember to do?* [Line up the decimal points so that you add tenths with tenths, hundredths with hundredths and so on.]
- *What percentage of £1 is £0.67?* [67%]
- *What fraction of 1 metre is 0.8m?* $[\frac{8}{10}$ or $\frac{4}{5}]$
- *How can you write 11 out of 20 as a percentage?* [Write it as the fraction $\frac{11}{20}$ and then change it to an equivalent fraction with the denominator 100 by multiplying both the numerator and denominator by 5 to give $\frac{55}{100}$ which is the percentage 55%.]

> **Key point:** Proportions of a whole can be described as fractions, as decimals and as percentages. Sometimes it is easier to work with fractions while at other times it may be easier to work with percentages or decimals.

🔍 Spot the mistake

Ask:

- *The statement says '20% of 55kg = $\frac{1}{5}$ of 55kg = 12kg'. Is this true?* [no]
- *What is wrong with the statement?* [It correctly shows that 20% is equivalent to $\frac{20}{100}$ which is $\frac{1}{5}$, but it incorrectly shows $\frac{1}{5}$ of 55kg as 12kg.]
- *What is the correct answer?* [11kg]

✅ Good to go?

Answers: a) 25%   **b)** 16%   **c)** 0.17   **d)** 0.75

> ## Pupil book practice   Pages 42 and 43
>
> This unit provides a variety of fraction, mixed number and decimal problems involving units of measurement and money. It includes a range of types of questions from the whole book and can serve as revision of many of the ideas encountered. The questions also test the pupils' understanding of the link between percentage, fraction and decimal equivalents.

→ Starting point

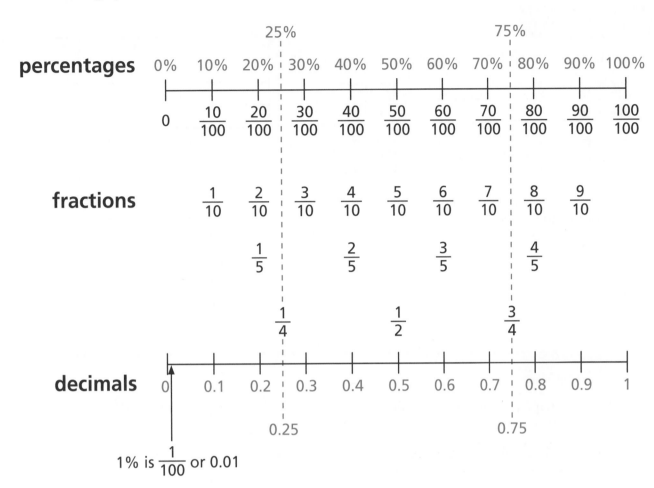

 Spot the mistake

20% of 55kg $= \frac{1}{5}$ of 55kg $=$ 12kg

✓ **Good to go?**

a) What percentage is equivalent to $\frac{1}{4}$?

b) What percentage of 1m is 0.16m?

c) What is $\frac{17}{100}$ as a decimal?

d) What is the total of 0.5 and 0.25?

Find equivalent fractions represented visually

Key point

Fractions that stand for the same amount are **equivalent**.

 $\frac{3}{4}$ is equivalent to $\frac{6}{8}$.

$\frac{2}{3}$ is equivalent to $\frac{6}{9}$.

Use the fraction wall to find equivalent fractions and answer the questions.

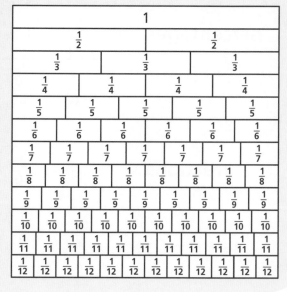

Get started

1 Tick the shape that shows a fraction equivalent to one-half.

☐   ☐   ✓

2 How many sixths are equivalent to $\frac{2}{3}$?

_____4_____ sixths

3 How many lots of $\frac{1}{12}$ are equivalent to one-half? _____6_____

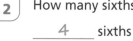

4 $\frac{1}{4}$ is equivalent to $\dfrac{3}{12}$.

5 The fraction $\frac{6}{10}$ is equivalent to how many fifths? _____3_____ fifths

6 Colour one-third of this shape.

7 True or false? $\frac{3}{4} = \frac{6}{10}$ True ☐   False ✓

8 $\frac{6}{8} = \dfrac{9}{12}$

Now try these

9 Write the fraction of each shape that is turquoise. Write a fraction with a different denominator each time.

a) $\dfrac{3}{5}$

b) $\dfrac{6}{10}$

c) $\dfrac{9}{15}$

10 A bar of chocolate has 10 chunks. Callum eats four-fifths of the whole bar.

How many chunks does he eat? _____8_____

11 A mango is cut into 12 equal pieces. Amy eats $\frac{5}{6}$ of the mango. How many pieces does she eat? _____10_____

12 6 out of 30 gems are turquoise. Joe says that one-fifth of the gems are turquoise. Is he correct?　Yes ✓　No ☐

13 True or false? $\frac{7}{10} = \frac{3}{4}$　　True ☐　False ✓

14 Is $\frac{7}{9}$ greater than, less than or equivalent to $\frac{2}{3}$?　_greater than_

15 $\frac{15}{20} = \dfrac{3}{4}$

16 How many hundredths is equivalent to one-quarter?　_25_ hundredths

17 $\frac{4}{5} = \dfrac{8}{10} = \dfrac{80}{100}$

18 This grid is made from 21 squares. Sophie colours 18 squares. She says that $\frac{18}{21}$ is equivalent to a number of sevenths. How many sevenths?　_6_ sevenths

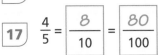

Challenge

19 Fill the gaps with the numbers 2, 8 and 12 to create two equivalent fractions.　$\dfrac{2}{8} = \dfrac{3}{12}$

20 Max has 100 marbles. $\frac{25}{100}$ are plain and $\frac{1}{4}$ have swirls. Does he have more, fewer or the same number of plain marbles as those with swirls?　_the same number_

21 True or false? These mixed numbers are equivalent: $1\frac{1}{5} = 1\frac{2}{10}$　True ✓　False ☐

22 Circle all the fractions that are equivalent to $\frac{8}{12}$.　$\frac{3}{4}$　$\left(\frac{2}{3}\right)$　$\left(\frac{4}{6}\right)$　$\frac{2}{5}$　$\left(\frac{6}{9}\right)$　$\frac{6}{8}$

23 A lorry driver stops for a break after $\frac{6}{10}$ of his journey. If his journey is 100 kilometres, after how many kilometres does he stop?　_60_ km

24 In a sports team $\frac{10}{12}$ are girls. Is it possible to group the team into three equal groups with two groups that are all girls and one group that is all boys?　Yes ☐　No ✓

25 Is it possible to replace the question marks in this statement with odd numbers so that it is true?
$\frac{?}{10}$ is equivalent to $\frac{?}{5}$.　Yes ☐　No ✓

26 Daisy notices that $\frac{3}{10}$ of some counters are yellow.
If there are 30 yellow counters, how many counters are there in total?　_100_

27 There are 50 children at a party. They play a game in which they split into five equal groups.
Every child in three of the groups wins a prize, so that $\frac{3}{5}$ of the children have a prize.
How many prizes are given out?　_30_

28 Gita knows that 0.6 is $\frac{6}{10}$ and that 0.60 is $\frac{60}{100}$. Is it true that 0.6 is equivalent to 0.60?　Yes ✓　No ☐

Find equivalent fractions using patterns

Key point

Fractions with the same value are **equivalent**.

If you multiply or divide both the numerator and denominator of a fraction by the same number, you will get an equivalent fraction.

Get started

1 Circle the fraction that is equivalent to $\frac{1}{2}$.

$\frac{1}{10}$　$\frac{2}{10}$　$\frac{3}{10}$　$\frac{4}{10}$　$\boxed{\frac{5}{10}}$

2 What is the missing equivalent fraction?

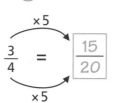

$\frac{3}{4} = \frac{15}{20}$

3 Find the equivalent fraction.

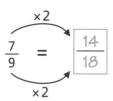

$\frac{7}{9} = \frac{14}{18}$

4 True or false? $\frac{2}{5} = \frac{4}{10}$

True ✓　False ☐

5 The numerator and denominator of $\frac{4}{5}$ are both multiplied by 4 to give what fraction?

$\frac{16}{20}$

6 The numerator and denominator of $\frac{44}{80}$ are both divided by 4 to give what fraction?

$\frac{11}{20}$

7 Multiply both numbers of the fraction $\frac{5}{6}$ by 7 to give an equivalent fraction.

$\frac{35}{42}$

8 How many tenths are equivalent to three-fifths? $\frac{3}{5} = \frac{6}{10}$

Now try these

9 What is the missing number? $\frac{5}{7}$ is equivalent to $\frac{50}{70}$.

10 12 of these 15 tennis balls are turquoise.
The balls are grouped into fifths.

How many fifths are turquoise? $\frac{12}{15} = \frac{4}{5}$

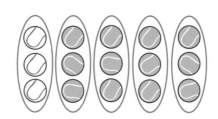

11 True or false? These three fractions are equivalent. $\frac{6}{8} = \frac{3}{4} = \frac{9}{12}$　True ✓　False ☐

12 Complete this pattern. $\frac{2}{3} = \frac{4}{6} = \frac{8}{12}$

13 Jack says that $\frac{36}{45}$ is equivalent to $\frac{4}{9}$. Is he correct?   Yes ☐   No ✓

14 Complete this pattern. $\frac{3}{12} = \frac{1}{4} = \frac{4}{16}$

15 Amber says that $\frac{8}{10}$ and $\frac{12}{15}$ are not equivalent. Is she correct?   Yes ☐   No ✓

16 Write a fraction equivalent to $\frac{32}{56}$ with the denominator 7. $\frac{4}{7}$

17 Circle the fraction that is not equivalent to the others in this list. $\frac{2}{5}$ $\frac{4}{10}$ $\frac{6}{15}$ $\frac{8}{20}$ ⟨$\frac{10}{30}$⟩

18 Write a fraction equivalent to $\frac{1}{3}$ with the denominator 27. $\frac{9}{27}$

Challenge

19 In a room, $\frac{7}{8}$ of the people are male. If there are 32 people, how many of them are male?   28

20 In a field, $\frac{4}{5}$ of the animals are sheep.
If there are 25 animals, how many of them are sheep?   20

21 There are 56 questions in a test. Dhruv answers $\frac{7}{8}$ of them correctly.
How many questions is this?   49

22 A grid of 24 squares has 18 coloured red. What proportion of the
squares are red? Give your answer as a fraction with the numerator 3. $\frac{3}{4}$

23 A motorcyclist stops after $\frac{3}{5}$ of her journey for a break. If her journey is
100 kilometres, after how many kilometres does she stop?   60 km

24 Fatima knows that 0.45 is $\frac{45}{100}$. How many twentieths is 0.45 equivalent to?

$0.45 = \frac{45}{100} = \frac{9}{20}$

25 In a badminton tournament three teams each play the same number of matches.
Team A wins $\frac{3}{8}$ of its matches, team B wins $\frac{2}{16}$ and team C wins $\frac{1}{4}$.
Which team wins most matches?   Team A

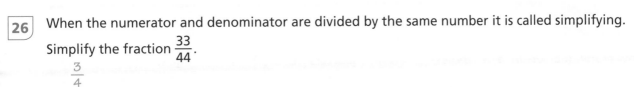

26 When the numerator and denominator are divided by the same number it is called simplifying.
Simplify the fraction $\frac{33}{44}$.
$\frac{3}{4}$

27 Simplify $\frac{28}{35}$. $\frac{4}{5}$

28 Circle all the fractions that simplify to $\frac{3}{5}$.   ⟨$\frac{15}{25}$⟩ $\frac{32}{40}$ $\frac{35}{45}$ ⟨$\frac{36}{60}$⟩   ⟨$\frac{30}{50}$⟩

Convert from mixed numbers to improper fractions

Key point

Mixed numbers are numbers that include a whole number and a fraction, such as $4\frac{3}{5}$.

The denominator (the bottom number) of the fraction shows how many equal parts each whole number has been split into. Here each whole is split into fifths.

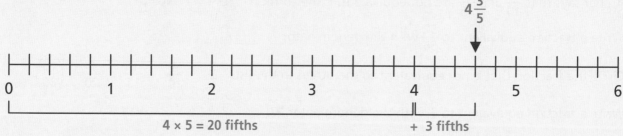

$4\frac{3}{5}$

$4 \times 5 = 20$ fifths　　　　　　　$+ 3$ fifths

To write a mixed number as an **improper fraction** (top-heavy fraction), multiply the whole number by the denominator and then add the numerator. This gives you the numerator of the improper fraction. The denominator stays the same.

$4\frac{3}{5} = \frac{23}{5}$　**Multiply the 4 by 5 to find how many fifths in 4 wholes and then add the 3.**

Get started

1 How many fifths in one whole?

____5____ fifths

2 How many lots of $\frac{1}{10}$ make one whole?

____10____

3 Each pizza is cut into eighths. How many eighths are there altogether here?

____24____ eighths

4 How many wholes can be made with 20 fifths? ____4____

5 How many halves in $2\frac{1}{2}$? $2\frac{1}{2} = \boxed{\dfrac{5}{2}}$

⭐⭐⭐

6 What mixed number does the arrow point to on this number line? ____$1\frac{1}{8}$____

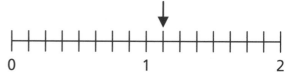

7 How many eighths in:

a) 1 whole? ____8____ eighths

b) $1\frac{1}{8}$? ____9____ eighths

8 How many sixths are there altogether in $2\frac{1}{6}$?

____13____ sixths

Now try these

9 How many quarters in: **a)** 3 wholes? ____12____ quarters **b)** $3\frac{3}{4}$? ____15____ quarters

10 How many fifths in $6\frac{2}{5}$? $6\frac{2}{5} = \boxed{\dfrac{32}{5}}$

11 Fill in the missing number. $2\frac{3}{5} = \boxed{\dfrac{13}{5}}$

12 True or false? $2\frac{1}{7}$ is equal to $\frac{16}{7}$. True ☐ False ✓

13 Circle the improper fraction that is equal to $2\frac{4}{5}$. $\frac{22}{5}$ $\frac{24}{5}$ $\left(\frac{14}{5}\right)$ $\frac{14}{4}$

14 Write $1\frac{1}{3}$ as an improper fraction. $\frac{4}{3}$

15 What is $7\frac{5}{6}$ as an improper fraction? $\frac{47}{6}$

5   6   7   8   9

16 What is the improper fraction equivalent to $3\frac{1}{100}$? $\frac{301}{100}$

17 Use the digits 7, 3 and 2 to write an improper fraction that has the same value as $3\frac{2}{7}$. $\frac{23}{7}$

18 True or false? $4\frac{5}{12} = \frac{52}{12}$ True ☐ False ✓

Challenge

19 Zac has 7 fruit cakes. He cuts each into 8 equal slices for a party. He then eats one of the slices. Are there enough slices left for 54 guests to each have a slice?

Yes ✓   No ☐

20 At an internet café it costs £1 for every quarter of an hour on the internet.

How much would you pay for $3\frac{3}{4}$ hours? £   15

21 When converting mixed numbers to improper fractions, Ben says that tenths and hundredths are special because the same digits are used in both. Are his examples all correct?

$2\frac{3}{10} = \frac{23}{10}$ $7\frac{9}{10} = \frac{79}{10}$ $1\frac{33}{100} = \frac{133}{100}$ $8\frac{67}{100} = \frac{867}{100}$ Yes ✓   No ☐

22 Use Ben's pattern to finish these. $4\frac{8}{10} = \frac{48}{10}$ $6.7 = \frac{67}{10}$ $5\frac{34}{100} = \frac{534}{100}$ $5.27 = \frac{527}{100}$

23 Leo jumps $4\frac{9}{10}$ m and Kai jumps $\frac{56}{10}$ m. How much further does Kai jump than Leo? $\frac{7}{10}$ m

24 A phone company charges 1p per tenth of a minute. How much does a $4\frac{3}{10}$ min call cost?   43   p

25 Find the difference between $9\frac{7}{9}$ and $\frac{88}{9}$.   0

26 A can of drink holds one-third of a litre. How many cans can be filled with $28\frac{2}{3}$ litres?   86

27 Lots of lorries are in a queue waiting to cross a bridge. The queue stretches for $2\frac{37}{40}$ km. If each lorry is $\frac{1}{40}$ km in length, what is the maximum number of lorries that could be in the queue?   117

28 Maryam has these 6 cards. Arrange the numbers on the cards to make a true statement.   4   5   6   8   9   9 $6\frac{4}{9} = \frac{58}{9}$

53

Convert from improper fractions to mixed numbers

Key point

Improper fractions are called top-heavy fractions because the numerator (top number) is larger than the denominator (bottom number), for example $\frac{23}{5}$.

To write an improper fraction as a **mixed number**, divide the numerator by the denominator. The answer is the whole number part of the mixed number and the remainder is the numerator of the fraction. The denominator stays the same.

$\frac{23}{5} = 4\frac{3}{5}$ Divide the numerator 23 by the denominator 5.
23 divided by 5 is **4 wholes** with **3 fifths** left over.

Get started

1 How many wholes are equal to 15 fifths? _____3_____

2 How many wholes is $\frac{4}{4}$? _____1_____

3 Each tart is cut into eighths. How many whole tarts is 16 eighths? ___2___

4 How many tenths in 4 wholes?

_____40_____ tenths

5 Seven-halves is the same as which mixed number? _____$3\frac{1}{2}$_____

6 Mark $\frac{12}{6}$ on this number line.

7 Mark $\frac{19}{6}$ on this number line.

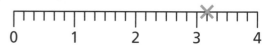

8 Write $\frac{19}{6}$ as a mixed number. _____$3\frac{1}{6}$_____

Now try these

9 Write five-quarters as a mixed number. _____$1\frac{1}{4}$_____

10 $\frac{11}{3} = \boxed{3\ \ \frac{2}{3}}$

11 $\frac{13}{4} = \boxed{3\ \ \frac{1}{4}}$

12 True or false? $\frac{17}{3}$ is equal to $5\frac{2}{3}$. True ☑ False ☐

13 Circle the mixed number that is equal to $\frac{13}{8}$. $1\frac{4}{8}$ $2\frac{5}{8}$ $1\frac{2}{8}$ $\boxed{1\frac{5}{8}}$ $1\frac{5}{6}$

14 True or false? $\frac{52}{8} = 6\frac{4}{8} = 6\frac{1}{2}$ True ✓   False ☐

15 Write $\frac{24}{7}$ as a mixed number. ___$3\frac{3}{7}$___

16 Mark $\frac{39}{6}$ on this number line.

$\begin{array}{ccccc} 5 & 6 & 7 & 8 & 9 \end{array}$

17 Use your answer for question 16 to complete the mixed number. $\frac{39}{6} = \boxed{6 \quad \frac{1}{2}}$

18 Write a mixed number that has the same value as $\frac{23}{3}$ using the digits 7, 3 and 2. ___$7\frac{2}{3}$___

Challenge

19 Thirty-two children each bring one-third of a litre of juice to make a fruit punch for the school fair. How many litres of punch can they make? ___$10\frac{2}{3}$___ l

20 At an internet café it costs £1 for every quarter of an hour on the internet. Jamie pays £17. How many hours does he pay for? ___$4\frac{1}{4}$___ hr

21 When converting improper fractions to mixed numbers, Cameron says that tenths and hundredths are special because the same digits are used in both. Are his examples all correct?

$\frac{43}{10} = 4\frac{3}{10}$ $\frac{71}{10} = 7\frac{1}{10}$ $\frac{136}{100} = 1\frac{36}{100}$ $\frac{807}{100} = 8\frac{7}{100}$ Yes ✓   No ☐

22 Complete these mixed numbers.

$\frac{43}{10} = \boxed{4 \quad \frac{3}{10}}$ $\frac{151}{10} = \boxed{15 \quad \frac{1}{10}}$ $\frac{223}{100} = \boxed{2 \quad \frac{23}{100}}$ $\frac{1250}{100} = \boxed{12 \quad \frac{50}{100}} = \boxed{12 \quad \frac{1}{2}}$

23 True or false? $\frac{65}{15} = 4\frac{5}{15} = 4\frac{1}{3}$ True ✓   False ☐

24 Find the difference between $\frac{71}{8}$ and $7\frac{7}{8}$. ___1___

25 A can of lemonade holds one-third of a litre. How many litres are there in 100 cans? ___$33\frac{1}{3}$___ l

26 A sewing machine makes stitches that are each $\frac{1}{8}$ of a centimetre long. If the machine makes a line of 42 stitches, with no gaps, how long is the line?

___$5\frac{2}{8}$___ cm   Also accept $5\frac{1}{4}$

27 A phone company charges 1p per tenth of a minute. Find the length of a call that costs 35p in minutes and seconds. ___3___ min ___30___ sec

28 Amir has these 6 cards. Arrange the numbers on the cards to make a true statement.

$\boxed{1}\ \boxed{2}\ \boxed{4}\ \boxed{5}\ \boxed{6}\ \boxed{7}$ $\dfrac{\boxed{4}\boxed{5}}{\boxed{6}} = \boxed{7}\dfrac{\boxed{1}}{\boxed{2}}$

55

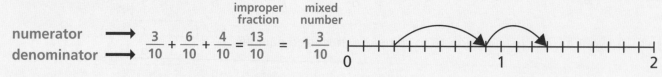

Add or subtract fractions with the same denominator

Key point

When adding or subtracting fractions, if the denominators are the same, **add or subtract the numerators only**. Use the same denominator. Some answers may be greater than 1. Such answers can be given as an **improper fraction** or a **mixed number**.

numerator ➝ $\dfrac{3}{10} + \dfrac{6}{10} + \dfrac{4}{10} = \overset{\text{improper fraction}}{\dfrac{13}{10}} = \overset{\text{mixed number}}{1\dfrac{3}{10}}$

denominator ➝

$\dfrac{11}{10} - \dfrac{6}{10} + \dfrac{2}{10} = \dfrac{7}{10}$ Look carefully at the **signs** to see if you must **add or subtract** each fraction.

Get started

1 Colour $\dfrac{1}{8}, \dfrac{3}{8}$ and $\dfrac{3}{8}$ of the rectangle.

How many eighths are now coloured?

___7___ eighths

2 $\dfrac{7}{10} + \dfrac{4}{10} + \dfrac{8}{10} = \boxed{\dfrac{19}{10}}$

3 $\dfrac{11}{7} - \dfrac{3}{7} = \boxed{\dfrac{8}{7}}$

4 $\dfrac{2}{9} + \dfrac{3}{9} - \dfrac{1}{9} = \boxed{\dfrac{4}{9}}$

5 Decrease by $\dfrac{9}{8}$ by $\dfrac{6}{8}$. ___$\dfrac{3}{8}$___

6 Give the total of $\dfrac{5}{6}, \dfrac{5}{6}$ and $\dfrac{3}{6}$ as an improper fraction. ___$\dfrac{13}{6}$___

7 Add $\dfrac{4}{5}$ to $\dfrac{4}{5}$ and then subtract $\dfrac{2}{5}$. Give your answer as a mixed number. ___$1\dfrac{1}{5}$___

8 $\dfrac{13}{12} - \boxed{\dfrac{11}{12}} = \dfrac{2}{12}$

Now try these

9 $\dfrac{15}{100} + \dfrac{5}{100} - \dfrac{11}{100} = \boxed{\dfrac{9}{100}}$

10 In a litter of kittens, $\dfrac{1}{7}$ of them are black, $\dfrac{2}{7}$ of them are ginger and the rest are brown. What fraction of the kittens are brown? ___$\dfrac{4}{7}$___

11 Find the values of a and b. $\dfrac{22}{10} - \dfrac{3}{10} = \dfrac{a}{10} = 1\dfrac{b}{10}$ a = ___19___   b = ___9___

12 Give the sum of five-sixths, two-sixths and ten-sixths as a mixed number. ___$2\dfrac{5}{6}$___

13 Write the answer as a mixed number. $\dfrac{4}{12} + \dfrac{9}{12} - \dfrac{4}{12} + \dfrac{10}{12} = \boxed{1 \dfrac{7}{12}}$

14 Three identical fractions have a total of $1\frac{4}{5}$.

What is each fraction? __$\frac{3}{5}$__

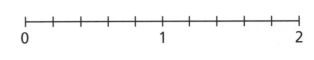

15 $\boxed{\frac{5}{15} = \frac{1}{3}}$ Use this fact to help you find the difference between $\frac{13}{15}$ and $\frac{1}{3}$. __$\frac{8}{15}$__

16 Subtract $\frac{3}{8}$ from $\frac{7}{8}$ and give your answer as an equivalent fraction with the numerator 1. __$\frac{1}{2}$__

17 $\boxed{\dfrac{17}{100} \quad \dfrac{15}{100} \quad \dfrac{19}{100} \quad \dfrac{24}{100} \quad \dfrac{21}{100}}$

Look at the fractions above. What is the largest fraction minus the smallest fraction? __$\frac{9}{100}$__

18 Subtract $\frac{12}{20}$ from $\frac{17}{20}$ and give your answer as an equivalent fraction with the numerator 1. __$\frac{1}{4}$__

Challenge

19 When $\frac{6}{10}$m is subtracted from $\frac{9}{10}$m, how much less than 2 metres is the result? __$1\frac{7}{10}$__ m

20 What mixed number is subtracted from the sum of $\frac{12}{9}$ and $\frac{3}{9}$ to give the answer $\frac{5}{9}$? __$1\frac{1}{9}$__

21 Write the answer as an improper fraction and as a mixed number. $\frac{21}{15} + \frac{9}{15} - \frac{11}{15}$

a) improper fraction __$\frac{19}{15}$__   b) mixed number __$1\frac{4}{15}$__

22 Zara uses $\frac{125}{100}$kg from a full 2kg bag of coffee.

What fraction of a kilogram is left? __$\frac{75}{100}$ or $\frac{3}{4}$__ kg

23 Jake jogs a distance of 10km in 1 hour. After 35 minutes he has jogged $\frac{7}{12}$ of the distance.

What fraction of the distance does he complete in the next 25 minutes? __$\frac{5}{12}$__

24 Peter spent $\frac{5}{12}$ of an hour watching a cartoon, $\frac{5}{12}$ of an hour watching a comedy and $\frac{6}{12}$ of an hour watching a quiz show.

a) What is the total time he spent watching these programmes? $\boxed{1\frac{4}{12}}$ hr $= \boxed{1\frac{1}{3}}$ hr

b) How many minutes is this? __80__ min

25 $\boxed{\frac{15}{24} = \frac{5}{8} \text{ and } \frac{2}{8} = \frac{1}{4}}$ Use these facts to help you find the sum of $\frac{15}{24}$ and $\frac{1}{4}$ in eighths. __$\frac{7}{8}$__

26 $\boxed{\frac{25}{60} = \frac{5}{12} \text{ and } \frac{6}{12} = \frac{1}{2}}$ Use these facts to help you find the sum of 25 minutes and half an hour. $\boxed{\dfrac{11}{12}}$ of an hour

27 Paige pours $\frac{5}{8}$ litres from a full litre jug of juice. What fraction of a litre is left? __$\frac{3}{8}$__ l

28 From a full 2-litre jug of water Sam pours $\frac{5}{4}$ litres.

What fraction of a litre is left? __$\frac{3}{4}$__ l

Add or subtract fractions with different denominators

Key point

When adding or subtracting fractions, if the denominators are the same, **add or subtract the numerators only**. Use the same denominator. If the denominators are not the same, first **change one or both fractions to an equivalent fraction to make the denominators the same**.

numerator $\longrightarrow$
denominator $\longrightarrow$ $\dfrac{1}{10} + \boxed{\dfrac{3}{5}} = \dfrac{1}{10} + \boxed{\dfrac{6}{10}} = \dfrac{7}{10}$

Change the fraction with the smaller denominator, if you only need to change one of them.

numerator $\longrightarrow$
denominator $\longrightarrow$ $\boxed{\dfrac{11}{12}} - \boxed{\dfrac{3}{8}} = \boxed{\dfrac{22}{24}} - \boxed{\dfrac{9}{24}} = \dfrac{13}{24}$

Get started

1 $\boxed{\dfrac{1}{2} \text{ is equivalent to } \dfrac{3}{6}.}$

Use this fact to find $\dfrac{1}{2} + \dfrac{1}{6}$. $\quad \dfrac{4}{6} \text{ or } \dfrac{2}{3}$

2 $\boxed{\dfrac{1}{2} \text{ is equivalent to } \dfrac{2}{4}.}$

Use this fact to find $\dfrac{1}{4} + \dfrac{1}{2}$. $\quad \dfrac{3}{4}$

3 Change $\dfrac{2}{5}$ to tenths to answer this question.

$\dfrac{2}{5} + \dfrac{3}{10} = \dfrac{?}{10} + \dfrac{3}{10} = \boxed{\dfrac{7}{10}}$

4 $\dfrac{3}{4} + \dfrac{1}{8} = \dfrac{?}{8} + \dfrac{1}{8} = \boxed{\dfrac{7}{8}}$

5 $\dfrac{4}{9} + \dfrac{1}{3} = \dfrac{4}{9} + \dfrac{?}{9} = \boxed{\dfrac{7}{9}}$

6 Change $\dfrac{5}{6}$ to twelfths to find the total of $\dfrac{5}{6}$ and $\dfrac{1}{12}$. $\quad \dfrac{11}{12}$

7 $\dfrac{1}{2} - \dfrac{1}{12} = \dfrac{?}{12} - \dfrac{1}{12} = \boxed{\dfrac{5}{12}}$

8 $\dfrac{1}{5} - \dfrac{1}{10} = \dfrac{?}{10} - \dfrac{1}{10} = \boxed{\dfrac{1}{10}}$

Now try these

9 $\dfrac{2}{3} - \dfrac{1}{12} = \boxed{\dfrac{8}{12}} - \dfrac{1}{12} = \boxed{\dfrac{7}{12}}$

10 What is the sum of $\dfrac{4}{5}$ and $\dfrac{1}{10}$? $\quad \dfrac{9}{10}$

11 Fill in the missing numbers. $\dfrac{3}{10} + \dfrac{5}{100} = \boxed{\dfrac{30}{100}} + \dfrac{5}{100} = \boxed{\dfrac{35}{100}}$

12 $\boxed{\dfrac{5}{15} = \dfrac{1}{3}}$ Use this fact to help you find the difference between $\dfrac{13}{15}$ and $\dfrac{1}{3}$. $\quad \dfrac{8}{15}$

13 True or false? $\frac{3}{4} - \frac{1}{8} = \frac{5}{8}$ True ✓ False ☐

14 Find the values of a, b and c. $\frac{9}{10} - \frac{1}{2} = \frac{9}{10} - \frac{a}{10} = \frac{b}{10} = \frac{c}{5}$

$a =$ ___5___ $b =$ ___4___ $c =$ ___2___

15 Give the sum of five-sixths and one-third as an improper fraction. ___$\frac{7}{6}$___

16 Write the answer as a mixed number. $\frac{4}{12} + \frac{3}{4} =$ $\boxed{1 \quad \frac{1}{12}}$

17 $\boxed{\frac{25}{60} = \frac{5}{12} \text{ and } \frac{1}{2} = \frac{6}{12}}$ Use these facts to help you find the sum of $\frac{25}{60}$ and $\frac{1}{2}$ in twelfths. ___$\frac{11}{12}$___

18 Subtract $\frac{1}{4}$ from $\frac{6}{8}$ and give your answer as an equivalent fraction with the numerator 1. ___$\frac{1}{2}$___

Challenge

19 $\frac{2}{9} + \frac{5}{9} - \frac{2}{3} =$ $\boxed{\frac{1}{9}}$

20 Change both fractions to twelfths to find the total. $\frac{1}{4} + \frac{1}{6} = \boxed{\frac{3}{12}} + \boxed{\frac{2}{12}} = \boxed{\frac{5}{12}}$

21 Li jogs $\frac{2}{5}$ km and then runs $4\frac{7}{10}$ km. How much more than 5km does she go in total?

Give your answer as: **a)** a fraction. ___$\frac{1}{10}$___ km **b)** a decimal. ___0.1___ km

22 Write the answer as an improper fraction and then as a mixed number.

$\frac{7}{5} + \frac{3}{5} + \frac{11}{15} = \boxed{\frac{41}{15}} = \boxed{2 \quad \frac{11}{15}}$

23 True or false? The answer to this question is zero. $\frac{2}{5} + \frac{3}{10} - \frac{1}{2} = ?$ True ☐ False ✓

24 Priya spent $\frac{5}{12}$ of an hour watching a cartoon, $\frac{5}{6}$ of an hour watching a comedy and $\frac{1}{4}$ of an hour

watching a quiz show. What is the total time she spent watching these? $\boxed{1 \quad \frac{6}{12}}$ hr $= \boxed{1 \quad \frac{1}{2}}$ hr

25 Seb pours $\frac{3}{10}$ litres (0.3l) from a full litre jug of juice into one glass and then

$\frac{33}{100}$ litres (0.33l) into another glass. What fraction of a litre remains in the jug? ___$\frac{37}{100}$___ l

26 Hayley has a 1kg bag of sugar. She uses $\frac{3}{5}$ kg (0.6kg) for some cakes and

then 0.35kg for some biscuits. What fraction of a kilogram of sugar is

left in the bag? ___$\frac{5}{100}$___ kg *Also accept* $\frac{1}{20}$

27 Change both fractions to twelfths to find the total. Then simplify the answer.

$\frac{2}{4} + \frac{1}{3} = \boxed{\frac{6}{12}} + \boxed{\frac{4}{12}} = \boxed{\frac{10}{12}} = \boxed{\frac{5}{6}}$

28 What is the sum of $\frac{3}{4}$ of an hour and $\frac{1}{3}$ of an hour? Give your answer as a mixed number. ___$1\frac{1}{12}$___ hr

Check-up test 1

1 What number is missing?

$\frac{3}{5}$ is equivalent to $\dfrac{6}{10}$.

1 mark

2 For each diagram write the fraction of the shape that is turquoise.
Write a fraction with a different denominator each time.

a) 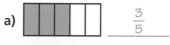 $\dfrac{3}{5}$

b) 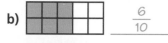 $\dfrac{6}{10}$

c) 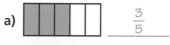 $\dfrac{9}{15}$

1 mark

1 mark

3 How many hundredths are equivalent to three-quarters? _____75_____ hundredths

1 mark

4 Theo notices that $\frac{9}{10}$ of some counters are orange.

If there are 90 orange counters, how many counters are there in total? ___100___

1 mark

5 True or false? $\frac{3}{5} = \frac{6}{10}$ True ✓   False ☐

1 mark

6 3 of these 15 golf balls are white.
The golf balls are grouped into fifths.

How many fifths are white? $\dfrac{3}{15} = \dfrac{1}{5}$

1 mark

7 Dev says that $\frac{6}{8}$ and $\frac{9}{12}$ are not equivalent. Is he correct?   Yes ☐   No ✓

1 mark

8 Write $\frac{12}{32}$ as an equivalent fraction with a denominator that is less than 10. $\dfrac{3}{8}$

1 mark

9 Each pizza is cut into eighths.
How many eighths are there altogether here? ___16___ eighths

1 mark

10 How many quarters in:

a) 4 wholes? ___16___ quarters

b) $2\frac{3}{4}$? ___11___ quarters

1 mark

11 True or false? $2\frac{1}{7}$ is equal to $\frac{15}{7}$.

True ✓   False ☐

1 mark

12 An internet café charges 1p per tenth of a minute.

How much does it cost to use the internet for $3\frac{7}{10}$ minutes? ___37___ p

1 mark

13 How many wholes are equal to 10 fifths? ___2___

14 True or false? $\frac{14}{3}$ is equal to $5\frac{1}{3}$.　　True ☐　False ✓

15 Ava uses the digits 1, 3 and 6 to write a mixed number that has the

same value as $\frac{19}{3}$. What is the mixed number? ___$6\frac{1}{3}$___

16 A phone company charges 1p per tenth of a minute. Find the length of a call that

costs 45p in minutes and seconds. ___4___ min ___30___ sec

17 $\frac{1}{9} + \frac{5}{9} - \frac{1}{9} = \boxed{\frac{5}{9}}$

18 On a bird table, $\frac{3}{8}$ of the birds are robins, $\frac{2}{8}$ of them are sparrows

and the rest are thrushes. What fraction of the birds are thrushes? ___$\frac{3}{8}$___

19 Subtract $\frac{14}{20}$ from $\frac{19}{20}$ and give your answer as

an equivalent fraction with the numerator 1. ___$\frac{1}{4}$___

20 Bella rows a distance of 10km in 1 hour. After 50 minutes she has

rowed $\frac{10}{12}$ of the distance. What fraction of the distance does she

row in the next 10 minutes? ___$\frac{2}{12}$ or $\frac{1}{6}$___

21 Complete this.

$\frac{2}{9} + \frac{2}{3} = \frac{2}{9} + \frac{?}{9} = \boxed{\frac{8}{9}}$

22 True or false? $\frac{7}{8} - \frac{1}{4} = \frac{5}{8}$

True ✓　False ☐

23 Write the answer as a mixed number.

$\frac{11}{12} + \frac{1}{4} = \boxed{1 \quad \frac{2}{12}}$ Also accept $1\frac{1}{6}$

24 What fraction of an hour is the sum of $\frac{3}{4}$ of an hour and $\frac{2}{3}$ of an hour?

Give your answer as a mixed number. ___$1\frac{5}{12}$___ hr

☐ 1 mark

☐ 1 mark

☐ 1 mark

☐ 1 mark

☐ 1 mark

☐ 1 mark

☐ 1 mark

☐ 1 mark

☐ 1 mark

☐ 1 mark

☐ 1 mark

☐ 1 mark

Total

☐

24 marks

Compare fractions with different denominators

Key point

When comparing fractions, if the denominators are the same, **compare the numerators only**.

If the denominators are not the same, first **change one or both fractions to an equivalent fraction to make the denominators the same**. This makes them easier to compare.

Which is larger?

numerator ⟶ $\frac{7}{10}$ or $\frac{3}{5}$ $\frac{7}{10}$ or $\frac{6}{10}$ $\frac{7}{10}$ is larger.
denominator ⟶

numerator ⟶ $\frac{11}{12}$ or $\frac{7}{8}$ $\frac{22}{24}$ or $\frac{21}{24}$ $\frac{11}{12}$ is larger.
denominator ⟶

Get started

1 Circle the fraction that is larger. $\left(\frac{4}{6}\right)$ $\frac{3}{6}$

2 Use < or > to show which is larger.

$\frac{5}{8}$ $\boxed{>}$ $\frac{4}{8}$

3 Given that $\frac{1}{2} = \frac{3}{6}$, circle the larger fraction.

$\frac{1}{2}$ $\left(\frac{4}{6}\right)$

4 Change $\frac{2}{5}$ to tenths to help you find the smaller fraction: $\frac{2}{5}$ or $\frac{3}{10}$.

$\frac{2}{5}$ or $\frac{3}{10}$ = $\frac{?}{10}$ or $\frac{3}{10}$ $\frac{3}{10}$

5 Given that $\frac{1}{3} = \frac{3}{9}$, circle the larger fraction.

$\frac{2}{9}$ $\left(\frac{1}{3}\right)$

6 True or false? $\frac{3}{4} > \frac{7}{8}$

$\frac{3}{4} > \frac{7}{8}$ $\frac{?}{8} > \frac{7}{8}$ True $\Box$ False $\boxed{\checkmark}$

7 Change $\frac{5}{6}$ to twelfths to help you find the larger fraction: $\frac{5}{6}$ or $\frac{9}{12}$. $\underline{\frac{5}{6} \text{ or } \frac{10}{12}}$

8 Which is smaller: $\frac{8}{20}$ or $\frac{1}{4}$? $\underline{\frac{1}{4} \text{ or } \frac{5}{20}}$

Now try these

9 True or false? $\frac{3}{4}$ is larger than $\frac{13}{20}$. True $\boxed{\checkmark}$ False $\Box$

10 Fill in the missing numbers. Write whether **a**, **b** or **c** is largest.

a) $\frac{2}{3} = \frac{\boxed{8}}{12}$ b) $\frac{5}{6} = \frac{\boxed{10}}{12}$ c) $\frac{1}{2} = \frac{\boxed{6}}{12}$ $\underline{\quad b \quad}$ is largest.

11 Use < or > to show which is larger. $\frac{6}{10}$ $\boxed{<}$ $\frac{4}{5}$

12 Which is larger: five-sixths or two-thirds? $\underline{\quad \text{five-sixths} \quad}$

13 Megan's red mug holds $\frac{3}{10}$ l and her blue mug holds $\frac{33}{100}$ l. Which holds more? $\underline{\quad \text{the blue mug} \quad}$

14 | $\frac{5}{15} = \frac{1}{3}$ | Use this fact to help you order the fractions from smallest to largest.

$\frac{7}{15}$　$\frac{1}{3}$　$\frac{4}{15}$　　$\frac{4}{15}$　　$\frac{1}{3}$　　$\frac{7}{15}$

15 Change the fractions to eighths and then write them in order from smallest to largest.

$\frac{3}{4}$　$\frac{5}{8}$　$\frac{1}{2}$　　$\frac{4}{8}$　　$\frac{5}{8}$　　$\frac{6}{8}$

16 Nicole wins some money in a competition. She gives $\frac{5}{12}$ of the money to her daughter and $\frac{1}{3}$ of the money to her niece. Who gets more: her daughter or her niece? ___her daughter___

17 Write these fractions in order from smallest to largest.

$\frac{3}{10}$　$\frac{1}{5}$　$\frac{17}{100}$　　$\frac{17}{100}$　　$\frac{1}{5}$　　$\frac{3}{10}$

18 Write < or > between these fractions so that the statement is true.　$\frac{1}{2}$ < $\frac{7}{12}$ < $\frac{3}{4}$

Challenge

19 True or false? $\frac{5}{8} > \frac{3}{4} > \frac{3}{8}$　　True ☐　False ✓

20 Order these fractions from largest to smallest.　$\frac{7}{18}$　$\frac{2}{3}$　$\frac{5}{9}$　　$\frac{2}{3}$　　$\frac{5}{9}$　　$\frac{7}{18}$

21 To get to school, Kirstin walks $\frac{4}{5}$ km, George walks $\frac{7}{10}$ km and Ella walks $\frac{13}{20}$ km.

a) Who walks the furthest? ___Kirstin___

b) Who walks the shortest distance? ___Ella___

22 A cartoon lasts for $\frac{5}{12}$ of an hour. A quiz lasts for $\frac{1}{3}$ of an hour. A comedy lasts for $\frac{3}{4}$ of an hour.

Which programme lasts longest? ___the comedy___

23 Fill in the missing digit so that the statement is true.　$\frac{1}{2}$ < $\frac{5}{8}$ < $\frac{3}{4}$

24 Tim uses $\frac{2}{5}$ kg of flour and then 0.35kg ($\frac{35}{100}$ kg) of sugar in a cake recipe.

Which does he use more of: flour or sugar? ___flour___

25 What is the missing digit?　$\frac{3}{4}$ < $\frac{4}{5}$ < $\frac{17}{20}$

26 | $\frac{7}{5}$　$\frac{30}{25}$　$\frac{66}{50}$　$\frac{13}{10}$ | Alice converts these fractions to hundredths to make them easier to compare.

Which of Alice's original fractions is:　a) largest? ___$\frac{7}{5}$___　b) smallest? ___$\frac{30}{25}$___

27 On a number line, which two fractions with the denominator 10 lie between $\frac{1}{2}$ and $\frac{3}{4}$? ___$\frac{6}{10}$___ ___$\frac{7}{10}$___

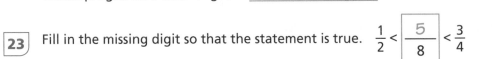

28 Which of these questions has the largest answer? Circle it.　$\left(\frac{1}{3} + \frac{3}{10}\right)$　$\frac{1}{6} + \frac{3}{15}$　$\frac{29}{30} - \frac{1}{2}$

Find fractions of numbers and quantities

Key point

To find a fraction of a quantity, divide the quantity by the denominator (to find one part) and multiply by the numerator (to find several parts).

numerator ➡ $\frac{5}{8}$ of 24　　Divide by 8 to find one-eighth.　$24 \div 8 = 3$
denominator ➡

Then multiply by 5 to find five-eighths.　$3 \times 5 = 15$

Alternatively, you can use equivalent fractions.　$\frac{5}{8} = \frac{?}{24}$ ↷ ×3　The missing number is 15.

Get started

1 If $\frac{1}{5}$ of 35cm is 7cm, what is $\frac{2}{5}$ of 35cm?

　　__14__ cm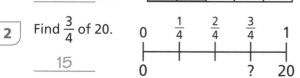

2 Find $\frac{3}{4}$ of 20.

　　__15__

3 Find $\frac{7}{10}$ of 30kg.　__21__ kg

4 Find $\frac{9}{10}$ of 50ml.　__45__ ml

5 Find $\frac{4}{7}$ of 35cm.

　　__20__ cm

6 True or false? $\frac{5}{8} = \frac{50}{80}$, so $\frac{5}{8}$ of 80 = 50

　　True ✓　False ☐

7 Given that $\frac{3}{8} = \frac{15}{40}$, find $\frac{3}{8}$ of £40.

　　£__15__

8 If $\frac{5}{6} = \frac{35}{42}$, what is $\frac{5}{6}$ of 42?　__35__

Now try these

9 True or false? $\frac{3}{7} = \frac{21}{49}$, so $\frac{3}{7}$ of 21 = 49　　True ☐　False ✓

10 Find seven-ninths of 36p.　__28__ p

11 How many minutes in $\frac{11}{12}$ of an hour? $\frac{11}{12} = \frac{?}{60}$　__55__ min

12 A full turn is 360°. How many degrees in $\frac{4}{6}$ of a full turn?

　　__240__ °

13 Heidi takes three-quarters of the money in each bag. How much does she take in total? £__57__

£48　£28

14 A young tiger is $\frac{9}{11}$ the height of his father. His father is 121cm tall.

a) How tall is the young tiger? _____99_____ cm

b) How many centimetres taller than the young tiger is his father? ___22___ cm

15 Seth draws a line that is $\frac{7}{8}$ the length of line A.

How long is Seth's line? ___21___ cm

Line A
_____

24cm

16 Urvi draws a line that is $\frac{3}{12}$ longer than line B.

How long is Urvi's line? ___45___ cm

Line B
_____

36cm

17 $\boxed{\frac{3}{8} = \frac{75}{200}}$ Use this fact to help you answer the question.

How much less than 2m is $\frac{3}{8}$ of 200cm? ___125___ cm

18 Fill in the missing number. $\boxed{\dfrac{5}{6}}$ of 48m = 40m

Challenge

19 Find the difference in kilograms between $\frac{3}{5}$ of 65kg and $\frac{5}{6}$ of 66kg. ___16___ kg

20 $\boxed{\dfrac{2}{3} \text{ of £270} \quad \dfrac{3}{8} \text{ of £400} \quad \dfrac{61}{100} \text{ of £300}}$

Look at the fractions above. What is the value of: a) the largest of these amounts? £ ___183___

b) the smallest of these amounts? £ ___150___   c) the total of these amounts? £ ___513___

21 47 hundredths = $\frac{47}{100}$ = 0.47. What is 47 hundredths of £200? £ ___94___

22 True or false? 0.45 of £200 = £90   True $\boxed{\checkmark}$ False $\boxed{}$

23 $\frac{1}{5}$ of an hour is 12 minutes. What fraction of an hour is 36 minutes? ___$\frac{3}{5}$___ hr

24 $\frac{1}{30}$ of an hour is 2 minutes. What fraction of an hour is 38 minutes? ___$\frac{19}{30}$___ hr

25 Find the difference between $\frac{6}{7}$ of 56 litres and $\frac{7}{8}$ of 56 litres. ___1___ l

26 David has £120. He gives $\frac{1}{3}$ of the money to his son and $\frac{3}{8}$ to his daughter.

How much more money does his daughter get than his son? £ ___5___

27 Josie has 54 doggy treats. She gives $\frac{1}{3}$ of the treats to Buster

and $\frac{5}{9}$ of them to Jess. How many treats are left? ___6___

28 The width of a rectangle is $\frac{5}{6}$ of its length. Its length is 72mm.

Find the perimeter of the rectangle in centimetres. ___26.4___ cm

Multiply fractions by whole numbers

Key point

When multiplying a fraction by a whole number, **multiply only the numerator by the whole number**. The denominator stays the same. So, if the fraction is thirds you end up with thirds or if the fraction is tenths you end up with tenths.

numerator $\longrightarrow$
denominator $\longrightarrow$ $\frac{3}{10} \times 3 = \frac{9}{10}$

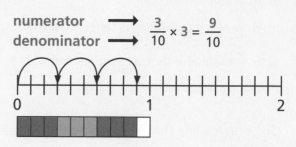

Some answers may be greater than 1. If so, the answers can be given as an improper fraction, a mixed number or a whole number.

improper fraction	mixed number			improper fraction	whole number
$\frac{5}{8} \times 9 = \frac{45}{8}$	$=$	$5\frac{5}{8}$		$\frac{5}{8} \times 8 = \frac{40}{8}$	$=$ $\quad 5$

Get started

1 $\frac{1}{8} + \frac{1}{8} + \frac{1}{8} = \boxed{\frac{3}{8}}$

2 How many fifths is $\frac{2}{5} \times 2$? $\boxed{\frac{4}{5}}$

3 Multiply $\frac{3}{7}$ by 2. $\boxed{\frac{6}{7}}$

4 Colour $\frac{2}{9}, \frac{2}{9}, \frac{2}{9}$ and $\frac{2}{9}$ of this square.
Then answer the question.

$\frac{2}{9} \times 4 = \boxed{\frac{8}{9}}$

5 True or false? Three lots of $\frac{3}{9}$ is one whole.

True $\boxed{\checkmark}$ False $\boxed{}$

6 Write the answer as an improper fraction:

$\frac{2}{3} \times 4 = \boxed{\frac{8}{3}}$

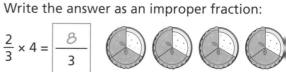

7 Find $\frac{5}{6} \times 3$.

Give your answer as an improper fraction. $\frac{15}{6}$

8 Find $\frac{2}{10} \times 3$. $\frac{6}{10}$

Now try these

9 True or false? $\frac{1}{3} \times 4 = \frac{4}{12}$ True $\boxed{}$ False $\boxed{\checkmark}$

10 Write the answer to $3 \times \frac{3}{5}$ as an improper fraction. $\frac{9}{5}$

11 Write the answer to $3 \times \frac{3}{5}$ as a mixed number. $1\frac{4}{5}$

12 What is $5 \times \frac{3}{4}$ as an improper fraction? _____ $\frac{15}{4}$ _____

13 Mark the answer to $\frac{3}{10} \times 6$ on this number line.

14 How many lots of $\frac{3}{4}$ makes $\frac{21}{4}$ or $5\frac{1}{4}$? _____ 7 _____

15 Circle which is more. ⟨$9 \times \frac{1}{5}$⟩ $\frac{2}{5} \times 4$

16 $\frac{20}{5}$ is equivalent to the whole number 4. What must you multiply $\frac{4}{5}$ by to get 4? _____ 5 _____

17 Jan walks $\frac{3}{12}$ km each day for 4 days. How many kilometres is this? _____ $\frac{12}{12}$ or 1 _____ km

18 Write the answer to $7 \times \frac{3}{10}$ as a mixed number. _____ $2\frac{1}{10}$ _____

Challenge

19 How much greater is $\frac{3}{8} \times 5$ than $5 \times \frac{2}{8}$? _____ $\frac{5}{8}$ _____

20 Ibrahim runs $\frac{3}{7}$ km each day for a week. How many kilometres does he run in total?

Write your answer as a whole number. _____ 3 _____ km

21 Mel's favourite song plays for $\frac{5}{6}$ of a minute. If Mel plays it 5 times in a row without

a gap, how long does this take? Give your answer as a mixed number. _____ $4\frac{1}{6}$ _____ min

22 Fill in the missing numbers to find the answer to the question in its simplest form.

$\frac{15}{100} \times 4 = \boxed{\dfrac{60}{100}} = \boxed{\dfrac{6}{10}} = \boxed{\dfrac{3}{5}}$

23 A carton of juice holds $\frac{33}{100}$ litre. How much less than one litre do three cartons hold? _____ $\frac{1}{100}$ _____ l

24 Mollie's stride is $\frac{3}{5}$ m. What is the length of 11 of her strides?

Give your answer as a mixed number. _____ $6\frac{3}{5}$ _____ m

25 Each episode of a TV series is $\frac{3}{4}$ hour. When watching the episodes without a break,

how many hours would it take to watch: **a)** 5 episodes? _____ $3\frac{3}{4}$ _____ hr **b)** 12 episodes? _____ 9 _____ hr

26 Nine people went out for pizza. Each person ate $\frac{5}{8}$ of a pizza.

What is the smallest number of pizzas that they could have bought? _____ 6 _____

27 On a number line, Hannah counts on from zero in equal steps of $\frac{7}{10}$. What number does she land on

after 7 steps? Give your answer as: **a)** a mixed number. _____ $4\frac{9}{10}$ _____   **b)** a decimal. _____ 4.9 _____

28 Given that $0.09 = \frac{9}{100}$, find the answer to 0.09×12. Give your answer as:

a) an improper fraction in hundredths.   **b)** a mixed number in hundredths.   **c)** a decimal.

a) _____ $\frac{108}{100}$ _____   **b)** _____ $1\frac{8}{100}$ _____   **c)** _____ 1.08 _____

Multiply fractions and mixed numbers by whole numbers

Key point

When multiplying a fraction by a whole number, **multiply only the numerator by the whole number.**
The denominator stays the same.

numerator $\longrightarrow$
denominator $\longrightarrow$ $\frac{2}{3} \times 5 = \frac{10}{3} = 3\frac{1}{3}$

When multiplying a mixed number, **multiply both parts separately and then add the answers together.**

$$2\frac{2}{3} \times 5 = (2 \times 5) + (\frac{2}{3} \times 5) = 10 + 3\frac{1}{3} = 13\frac{1}{3}$$

Get started

1 $\frac{1}{2} \times 5 = \frac{5}{2} = \boxed{2 \quad \frac{1}{2}}$

2 $\frac{1}{2} \times 7 = \boxed{\frac{7}{2}} = \boxed{3 \quad \frac{1}{2}}$

3 $\frac{3}{4} \times 3 = \boxed{\frac{9}{4}} = \boxed{2 \quad \frac{1}{4}}$

4 Multiply $\frac{1}{5}$ by 6. Give your answer as a mixed number.

$\boxed{1 \quad \frac{1}{5}}$

5 What is $\frac{2}{5} \times 4$ written as a mixed number?

$\boxed{1 \quad \frac{3}{5}}$

6 Write $\frac{3}{10} \times 7$ as a mixed number. $\boxed{2 \quad \frac{1}{10}}$

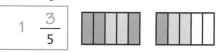

0　　　　　　　　1　　　　　　　　2

7 Colour $\frac{2}{9} \times 4$ on this grid.

8 Count the stars to find the answer.

$1\frac{1}{2} \times 3 = \boxed{4 \quad \frac{1}{2}}$

Now try these

9 Count the doughnuts to find the answer. $1\frac{1}{4} \times 3 = \boxed{3 \quad \frac{3}{4}}$

10 Fill in the missing numbers. $1\frac{2}{9} \times 4 = (1 \times 4) + (\frac{2}{9} \times 4) = \boxed{4} + \boxed{\frac{8}{9}} = \boxed{4 \quad \frac{8}{9}}$

11 $3\frac{1}{3} \times 2 = (3 \times 2) + (\frac{1}{3} \times 2) = \boxed{6} + \boxed{\frac{2}{3}} = \boxed{6 \quad \frac{2}{3}}$

12 $2\frac{1}{4} \times 3 = (2 \times 3) + (\frac{1}{4} \times 3) = \boxed{6} + \boxed{\frac{3}{4}} = \boxed{6 \quad \frac{3}{4}}$

13 $4\frac{1}{2} \times 3 = (4 \times 3) + (\frac{1}{2} \times 3) = \boxed{12} + \boxed{1 \quad \frac{1}{2}} = \boxed{13 \quad \frac{1}{2}}$

14 Mark the answer on this line.

$1\frac{3}{4} \times 3 = (1 \times 3) + (\frac{3}{4} \times 3) =$

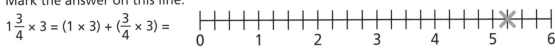

0   1   2   3   4   5   6

15 $5\frac{3}{8} \times 2 = (\boxed{5} \times 2) + (\boxed{\frac{3}{8}} \times 2) = 10 + \boxed{\frac{6}{8}} = \boxed{10 \frac{6}{8}}$

16 Multiply $5\frac{3}{10}$ by 3. Write the answer as a mixed number. $15\frac{9}{10}$

17 What is three and four-ninths multiplied by 2? $6\frac{8}{9}$

18 Fill in the missing numbers to find $2\frac{2}{5} \times 3$.

$2\frac{2}{5} \times 3 = (\boxed{2} \times 3) + (\boxed{\frac{2}{5}} \times 3) = \boxed{6} + \boxed{1 \frac{1}{5}} = \boxed{7 \frac{1}{5}}$

Challenge

19 What is $7 \times 1\frac{3}{10}$? Write the answer as a mixed number. $9\frac{1}{10}$

20 Amelie cycled $1\frac{1}{6}$ km each day for a week.

How many kilometres did she cycle in total? $8\frac{1}{6}$ km

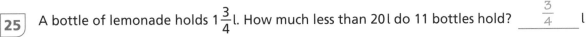

21 Find nine lots of $2\frac{3}{4}$ kg. $24\frac{3}{4}$ kg

$2\frac{3}{4}$ kg

22 How much greater is $1\frac{3}{5} \times 4$ than $3 \times 1\frac{4}{5}$? 1

23 Find the product of $3\frac{2}{3}$ and 6. Give your answer as a whole number. 22

24 A printing press takes $1\frac{5}{6}$ minutes to print 1 book. How long does it take to print 10 books?

a) Give your answer as a mixed number. $18\frac{2}{6}$ min   *Also accept* $18\frac{1}{3}$

b) Give your answer in minutes and seconds. 18 min 20 sec

25 A bottle of lemonade holds $1\frac{3}{4}$ l. How much less than 20 l do 11 bottles hold? $\frac{3}{4}$ l

26 Some cubes are each $8\frac{7}{10}$ cm (8.7cm) tall. If seven cubes are stacked to make a tower,

how tall is the tower as: a) a mixed number? $60\frac{9}{10}$ cm   b) a decimal? 60.9 cm

27 Arrange the digits 3, 5 and 6 into these boxes so that the multiplication makes the largest answer possible. Then write the answer.

$\boxed{5\frac{2}{3}} \times \boxed{6} = \underline{34}$

28 Fill in the missing numbers. $\boxed{3\frac{4}{5}} \times 7 = 21 + \boxed{\frac{28}{5}} = 21 + 5\frac{3}{5} = 26\frac{3}{5}$

Round decimals to the nearest whole number and tenth

Key point

The digits after the decimal point are called **decimal places**. A number like 3.42 has two decimal places. The headings in the grid stand for **ones**, **tenths** and **hundredths**.

O	.	t	h
3	.	4	2

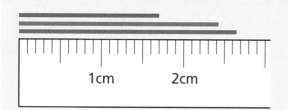

When rounding decimals to the **nearest whole number**, look at the **tenths** digit. If it is 5 or more, round up. If not, round down.

1.7 → 2   2.43 → 2

When rounding decimals to the **nearest tenth (to one decimal place)**, look at the **hundredths** digit. If it is 5 or more, round up. If not, round down.

2.43 → 2.4   2.65 → 2.7

Get started

1 Mark 0.6 on this number line.

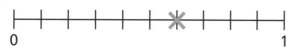

2 Look at the number line. Is 0.6 nearer to 0 or 1? _____1_____

3 Which whole number is 5.8 closest to: 5 or 6? _____6_____

4 Round 7.9 to the nearest whole number. _____8_____

5 What is 8.2 rounded to the nearest whole number? _____8_____

6 Circle the tenths digit in this number. 5 . ④ 9

7 Is the tenths digit of 5.49 five or higher?

Yes ☐   No ✓

8 True or false? 5.49 is 5 when rounded to the nearest whole number.

True ✓   False ☐

Now try these

9 Is the tenths digit of 3.72 five or higher?   Yes ✓   No ☐

10 What is 3.72 rounded to the nearest whole number? _____4_____

11 What is 2.99 rounded to the nearest whole number? _____3_____

12 Which whole number is 3.21 closest to? _____3_____

13 A baby weighs 7.5kg. What is this weight rounded to the nearest whole kilogram? _____8_____kg

14 Circle the decimal that is 6 when rounded to the nearest whole number.

4.9   5.3   6.7   6.5   (5.6)

15   Circle the two decimals that are 4 when rounded to the nearest whole number.

4.91   (3.73)   5.03   4.50   3.45   (4.09)

16   Mark the decimal 3.72 on this line.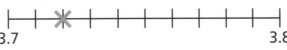

3.7   3.8

17   Is the hundredths digit of the decimal 3.72 five or higher?   Yes ☐   No ✓

18   What is 3.72 rounded to one decimal place?   _3.7_

Challenge

19   Fill in the gaps in the table.

decimal	to the nearest tenth
3.46	3.5
2.71	2.7
6.85	6.9

20   When rounded to the nearest tenth of a kilogram, what does 9.52kg round to?   _9.5_ kg

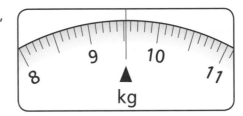

21   True or false? 5.29 is 5 when rounded to the nearest tenth.   True ☐   False ✓

22   Is 3.36m closer to: **a)** 3m or 4m?   _3_ m   **b)** 3.3m or 3.4m?   _3.4_ m

23   Round 5.38 to: **a)** the nearest whole number.   _5_   **b)** the nearest tenth.   _5.4_

24   Is £7.74 million closer to: **a)** £7 million or £8 million? £ _8_ million

b) £7.7 million or £7.8 million? £ _7.7_ million

25   What is the smallest decimal with two decimal places that, when rounded to the nearest tenth, is 2.8?   _2.75_

26   Circle all the decimals that round to 5.0 when rounded to the nearest tenth.

(4.98)   4.91   5.20   5.31   5.06   (5.02)

27   Round 9.49 to: **a)** the nearest whole number.   _9_   **b)** one decimal place.   _9.5_

28   Fill in the gaps in the table.

decimal	to the nearest whole number	to one decimal place
6.02	6	6.0
8.55	9	8.6
9.98	10	10.0

Understand thousandths as fractions and decimals

Key point

The digits that come after the decimal point stand for **tenths, hundredths, thousandths** and so on. The position of the **last digit** in the decimal indicates whether you have tenths, hundredths or thousandths.

O	.	t	h	th	
0	.	7			$= \dfrac{7}{10}$
1	.	2	1		$= \dfrac{121}{100}$
0	.	0	1	4	$= \dfrac{14}{1000} = \dfrac{7}{500}$
0	.	3	7	5	$= \dfrac{375}{1000} = \dfrac{75}{200} = \dfrac{3}{8}$

Remember that zeros on the end of a decimal are unimportant, so 0.100 is the same as 0.10 and 0.1. This means that **100 thousandths** are equal to **10 hundredths** and **1 tenth**.

Get started

1 How many tenths are equal to 0.4? $\dfrac{4}{10}$

2 Write 0.9 as a fraction. $\dfrac{9}{10}$

3 True or false? 1.3 = one and three-tenths

True ✓   False ☐

4 Six-hundredths of this square is turquoise. Write this as a decimal in the place value grid below.

O	.	t	h
0	.	0	6

5 Write 0.03 as a fraction. $\dfrac{3}{100}$

6 How many hundredths is equal to 0.11? $\dfrac{11}{100}$

7 Write $\dfrac{16}{100}$ as a decimal.

0.16

8 Write the next two decimals in this pattern.

0.08, 0.09, 0.10, 0.11, _0.12_ , _0.13_

Now try these

9 How many thousandths are equal to 0.003? 0.003 = $\dfrac{3}{1000}$

10 What is seven-thousandths as a decimal? _0.007_

11 True or false? 4 tenths and 5 hundredths = 45 hundredths = 0.45   True ✓   False ☐

12 How many thousandths are equal to 0.025? 0.025 = $\dfrac{25}{1000}$

13 What is the missing number? $0.103 = \boxed{103}$ thousandths $= \dfrac{103}{1000}$

14 Write $\dfrac{47}{1000}$ as a decimal. __0.047__

15 True or false? 1 tenth, 6 hundredths and 1 thousandth $= \dfrac{161}{1000} = 0.161$ True ☑   False ☐

16 Mark 0.07 and 0.14 on this line.

$0 \quad \dfrac{1}{100}$ $\qquad \dfrac{10}{100}$ $\qquad \dfrac{20}{100}$

17 What decimal less than 1 has no ones, 1 tenth and 7 thousandths? __0.107__

18 There are 1000 metres in 1 kilometre. **a)** What fraction of 1 kilometre is 249 metres? $\dfrac{249}{1000}$ km

b) What is this fraction as a decimal? __0.249__ km

Challenge

19 Mark 0.604 and 0.619 on this line.

$\dfrac{600}{1000}$ $\qquad\qquad \dfrac{610}{1000}$ $\qquad\qquad \dfrac{620}{1000}$

20 The line is $\dfrac{23}{1000}$ of a metre. Write its length using whole numbers or decimals:

a) in millimetres. __23__ mm

b) in centimetres. __2.3__ cm

c) in metres. __0.023__ m

1cm   2cm

21 Circle the decimal that is equal to $\dfrac{17}{10}$.   0.17   0.017   (1.7)

22 What fraction of a metre is 0.75m? Give your answer with the denominator 4. $\dfrac{3}{4}$ m

23 In a school there are 1000 children. 489 of the children are girls. As a decimal, what proportion of all the children are:

a) girls? __0.489__   **b)** boys? __0.511__

24 How many thousandths must be added to 0.999 to make 1 whole? $0.999 + \dfrac{\boxed{1}}{1000} = 1$

25 Fill in the missing numbers. $\dfrac{1}{5} = \dfrac{\boxed{2}}{10} = \dfrac{\boxed{20}}{100} = 0.2 = 0.20$

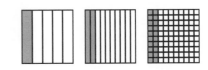

26 Reuben says that $\dfrac{9}{10}$m is equivalent to $\dfrac{90}{100}$m. Is he correct?   Yes ☑   No ☐

27 Fill in the missing numbers. $0.80 = \dfrac{\boxed{80}}{100} = \dfrac{\boxed{8}}{10} = \dfrac{\boxed{4}}{5}$

28 Write 0.125 as a fraction with the denominator 8. $\dfrac{125}{1000} = \dfrac{5}{40} = \dfrac{\boxed{1}}{8}$

Check-up test 2

1 Use < or > to show which fraction is larger. $\frac{6}{8}$ < $\frac{7}{8}$

1 mark

2 Laura's red mug holds $\frac{7}{10}$ litres and her blue mug holds $\frac{77}{100}$ litres.

Which mug holds more? _the blue mug_

1 mark

3 Charlie went shopping. He spent $\frac{4}{12}$ of his money in the butcher's and $\frac{1}{4}$ of his money in the baker's.

In which shop did he spend more? _the butcher's_

1 mark

4 Order these fractions from largest to smallest.

$\frac{9}{16}$ $\frac{5}{8}$ $\frac{3}{4}$ $\frac{3}{4}$ $\frac{5}{8}$ $\frac{9}{16}$

1 mark

5 What is $\frac{7}{10}$ of 50ml? _35_ ml

1 mark

6 A full turn is 360°.

How many degrees in $\frac{2}{6}$ of a full turn? _120_ °

1 mark

7 Ali draws a line that is $\frac{5}{8}$ the length of line A.

Line A

How long is Ali's line? _15_ cm

24cm

1 mark

8 $\frac{1}{30}$ of an hour is 2 minutes. What fraction of an hour is 14 minutes? _$\frac{7}{30}$_ hr

1 mark

9 Find four lots of $\frac{1}{5}$. _$\frac{4}{5}$_

1 mark

10 Colour $\frac{3}{12}$ × 3 on the grid.

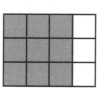

1 mark

11 Write the answer to 4 × $\frac{3}{5}$ as an improper fraction. _$\frac{12}{5}$_

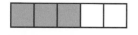

1 mark

12 Write the answer to 9 × $\frac{3}{10}$ as a mixed number. _$2\frac{7}{10}$_

1 mark

13 Ellie's stride measures $\frac{4}{5}$ m. What is the length of 9 of her strides?

Give your answer as a mixed number. ____$7\frac{1}{5}$____ m

1 mark

14 $4\frac{1}{3} \times 2 = (4 \times 2) + (\frac{1}{3} \times 2) =$ | $8 \quad \frac{2}{3}$ |

1 mark

15 Write the answer to $5 \times 1\frac{7}{10}$ as a mixed number. ____$8\frac{5}{10}$____ Also accept $8\frac{1}{2}$

1 mark

16 A bottle holds $1\frac{1}{4}$ litres. How much less than 17 litres do 13 bottles hold? ____$\frac{3}{4}$____ l

1 mark

17 What is 7.6 rounded to the nearest whole number? ____8____

1 mark

18 Give 4.38 as a decimal rounded to the nearest tenth. ____4.4____

1 mark

19 Round 8.52 to the nearest whole number. ____9____

1 mark

20 What is the smallest decimal with two decimal
places that, when rounded to the nearest tenth, is 3.4? ____3.35____

1 mark

21 How many tenths are equal to 0.6?

$0.6 = \dfrac{6}{10}$

1 mark

22 What is nine-thousandths as a decimal? ____0.009____

1 mark

23 Write $\frac{74}{1000}$ as a decimal. ____0.074____

1 mark

24 1000 children attend a classical musical concert. 624 of the children are girls.
As a decimal, what proportion of all the children are:

a) girls? ____0.624____

b) boys? ____0.376____

1 mark

Total

24 marks

Compare decimals with up to three decimal places

Key point

When comparing decimals, remember that tenths are larger than hundredths and hundredths are larger than thousandths. Compare the digits from left to right.

O	.	t	h	th
0	.	0	8	6
0	.	1	2	5

0.125 is larger than 0.086.

0.125 > 0.086

It can help to write zeros on the end of decimals so that the decimals being compared have the same number of decimal places. This makes them easier to compare.

0.94 > 0.913   **can be written as**   0.94**0** > 0.913

Get started

1 Which is greater:

0.16 or 0.61?   _0.61_

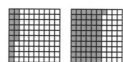

2 Which is greater: 0.24 or 0.42?   _0.42_

3 Circle the larger amount of money.

(£0.30) £0.03

4 Put the decimals in order from smallest to largest.   0.74   0.80   0.79

_0.74_   _0.79_   _0.80_

5 Use < or > to show which is larger.

0.837 [<] 0.983

6 Given that 0.2 is equal to 0.20, circle the larger number.

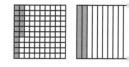

0.16   (0.2)

7 Circle the tenths digit in each of these decimals.   0 . (7)   0 . (6) 9

8 Which of these two numbers has more tenths: 0.7 or 0.69?   _0.7_

Now try these

9 Circle the larger number: (0.7)   0.69

10 Which is the shorter length: 0.99m or 0.9m?   _0.9_ m

11 Which is smaller: 0.5 or 0.51?   _0.5_

12 Freddie says that, because 7.6 and 7.60 are the same number, then 7.6 is larger than 7.58. Is he correct?

Yes [✓]   No [ ]

13 Write the weights of these bags in order from lightest to heaviest.

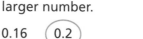

0.573 kg   0.375 kg   0.735 kg   0.753 kg   0.537 kg   0.357 kg

_0.357_ kg   _0.375_ kg   _0.537_ kg   _0.573_ kg   _0.735_ kg   _0.753_ kg

14   Circle the larger number.   0.582   (0.61)

15   Use < or > to show which is larger.   0.99   >   0.818

16   True or false? 0.912 is greater than 0.8.   True ✓   False ☐

17   Write a number with two decimal places that lies between 0.469 and 0.471.   _0.47_

18   True or false? 0.685 < 0.69   True ✓   False ☐

Challenge

19   Three potatoes each weigh 0.096kg, 0.13kg and 0.2kg.

What is the weight of the heaviest potato?   _0.2_ kg

20   True or false? 0.625 > 0.75 > 0.375   True ☐   False ✓

21   Here are the race times of three runners. Tick the fastest time.

22.463 seconds ✓   22.47 seconds ☐   22.5 seconds ☐

22   Put these decimals in order from smallest to largest.

0.5   0.551   0.55   0.05   0.005   _0.005_   _0.05_   _0.5_   _0.55_   _0.551_

23   The River Caiton is 0.64km at its widest point. The River Kean is 0.594km at its widest point.

Which is the wider river?   _River Caiton_

24   Some athletes are doing the long jump. The distances jumped are shown below.

Kate 7.3m   Lucy 6.87m   Noah 7.02m   Luke 6.9m

Put the jumps in order from smallest to largest.

_6.87_ m   _6.9_ m   _7.02_ m   _7.3_ m

25   What is the smallest decimal with three decimal places that is greater than the number 3?   _3.001_

26   Maya puts some capacities in order, from least to most, but has made one mistake.
Cross out the capacity that is in the wrong place.

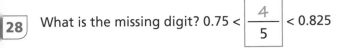

0.02 litres   0.021 litres   0.2 litres   0.201 litres   0.202 litres   0.22 litres   ~~0.122 litres~~

27   There are two bridges across part of a river. The first bridge is 24.53m long and the second bridge is 24.5m long. How much longer is the first bridge than the second bridge? Give your answer:

a) in metres.   _0.03_ m   **b)** in centimetres.   _3_ cm

28   What is the missing digit? 0.75 < $\frac{4}{5}$ < 0.825

Solve problems with decimals up to three decimal places

Key point

When adding and subtracting decimals, **line up the decimal points** so that you add thousandths to thousandths, hundredths to hundredths, and tenths to tenths.

O	.	t	h	th
0	.	4	0	
+ 0	.	3	7	
= 0	.	7	7	

O	.	t	h	th
0	.	4^3	$^1\cancel{0}^9$	$^1 0$
− 0	.	3	7	5
= 0	.	0	2	5

It can help to write zeros on the end of decimals so that the decimals being added or subtracted have the same number of decimal places. This makes them easier to add or subtract.

Get started

1 Mark a cross on the ruler to show 1.8cm.

1cm   2cm   3cm

2 Write $3\frac{7}{10}$ cm as a decimal. __3.7__ cm

3 What is the sum of £0.50 and £0.06?

£ __0.56__

4 How many tenths are equal to three-tenths plus seven-tenths? __10__ tenths

5 What is 1.3 + 0.7? __2 or 2.0__

6 Write $\frac{1}{4}$ as a decimal.

__0.25__

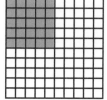

7 True or false? $3\frac{1}{100}$ m = 3m and 1cm = 3.01m

True ✓   False ☐

8 0.9kg + | 0.2 | kg = 1.1kg

Now try these

9 How many quarters of a kilogram are in 0.75 kilograms? __3__ quarters

10 0.7kg of flour and some sugar are put into a bowl.
The flour and sugar together weigh 1.2kg.

How much sugar is there? __0.5__ kg

11

	0 .	4
+ 3 .	4	2
3 .	4	6

Has this calculation been done correctly?

Yes ☐   No ✓

12 Add 4.15km and 3.62km. __7.77__ km

13 What is the difference between 0.8m and 0.75m? __0.05__ m

14 In a game of cricket, Aiden hits the ball 4.9m and Ahmed hits it 5.6m.
How much further does Ahmed hit the ball than Aiden? __0.7__ m

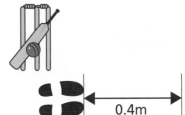

15 Each of Mia's steps is 0.4m apart when she walks. If she
takes three steps, how far from the start has she walked? __1.2__ m

0.4m

16 Some athletes are doing the long jump. Here are the distances each jumps.
Ollie 4.74m   Jon 4.69m   Carl 4.7m
a) How much further does Ollie jump than Jon? __0.05__ m
b) How much further does Ollie jump than Carl? __0.04__ m
c) How much further does Carl jump than Jon? __0.01__ m

17 Find the total mass of these three parcels. __4.875__ kg

1.5 kg   1.125 kg   2.25 kg

18 Some square tiles have sides that are each 0.55m. How long is a line of three touching tiles, in metres?
Give your answer as a decimal. __1.65__ m

Challenge

19 Put a decimal point in each of these numbers so that the value of the 4 is 4 ones.

6 5 4.3   2 4.9 6   4.2 6 7

20 Now find the sum of the three numbers you made in question 19. __683.527__

21 Find the difference between (4.0 + 6.0) and (0.4 + 0.6). __9__

22 Write the decimal that is halfway between 0.4 and 0.38. __0.39__

23 | 0.9   0.01   0.25   0.09   0.75 |

Look at the decimals above. Which two of these decimals when added together equal:
a) one whole? __0.25__ and __0.75__   b) one-tenth? __0.01__ and __0.09__

24 Write the difference between 0.1 and a half as a decimal. __0.4__

25 | 0.3km   0.15km   0.09km   1.1km   0.999km |

Look at the lengths above. Add the shortest length to the longest length. __1.19__ km

26 How much more does the white tin hold than the turquoise tin?
Give your answer: a) in litres. __0.037__ l   b) in millilitres. __37__ ml

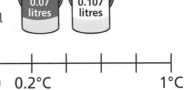

0.07 litres   0.107 litres

27 What is 0.2°C minus 0.6°C? __−0.4__ °C

−1°C   0   0.2°C   1°C

28 A rectangle has a length of 0.4m and a width that is 5cm less than its length.
What is the perimeter of the rectangle? __1.5__ m

Understand percentages as fractions

Key point

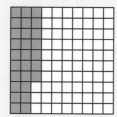

This is the **percentage symbol**. The **percentage symbol** stands for 'per cent' which means 'out of 100'. So **27%** means '**27 out of 100**' or $\frac{27}{100}$ or **27 hundredths**.

27% of the grid is turquoise.

73% of the grid is white.

100% is the whole of the grid.

Get started

1 True or false? 38% means $\frac{38}{100}$.

True ✓   False ☐

2 Write 49% as a fraction with the denominator 100. $\frac{49}{100}$

3 85 out of these 100 squares are turquoise. What percentage is turquoise?   _85%_

4 What percentage is equal to $\frac{59}{100}$? Remember to include the percentage symbol.   _59%_

5 Fill in the missing percentage.

$\frac{70}{100}$ = 70 %

6 If 95% of a shape is purple, what percentage is not purple?   _5%_

7 $\frac{6}{100}$ = 6 %

8 Given that $\frac{1}{2} = \frac{50}{100}$, what is $\frac{1}{2}$ as a percentage?   _50%_

Now try these

9 61% of the people at a concert were adults. What percentage were children?   _39%_

10 Seventy-three out of one hundred cards in a shop are birthday cards. Write this as a fraction

and as a percentage. $\frac{73}{100}$ = 73 %

11 In a cinema there are 100 seats. 42% of the seats are empty. What percentage of the seats are not empty?   _58%_

12 True or false? 30% + 70% = 100% = 1 whole   True ✓   False ☐

13 Fill in the missing numbers.

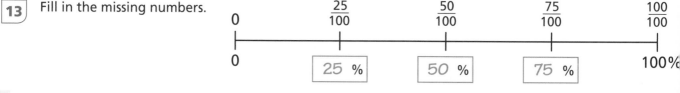

14 Write A and B as fractions with the denominator 100.   A = $\frac{40}{100}$ B = $\frac{90}{100}$

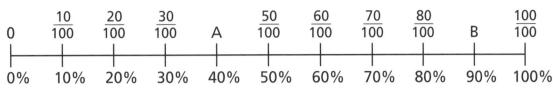

| 0 | $\frac{10}{100}$ | $\frac{20}{100}$ | $\frac{30}{100}$ | A | $\frac{50}{100}$ | $\frac{60}{100}$ | $\frac{70}{100}$ | $\frac{80}{100}$ | B | $\frac{100}{100}$ |

0%   10%   20%   30%   40%   50%   60%   70%   80%   90%   100%

15 True or false? If Katya has used 50% of the cream in a 100ml pot, she has used half of the cream.

True ✓   False ☐

16 Alfie has a full jug of milk. He pours 40% of it into a cup.
What percentage of the jug is filled now?   _60%_

17 Adele gives 11% of her wages to her son, 19% to her daughter and spends
the rest herself. What percentage does she spend herself?   _70%_

18 What percentage of one metre is 15cm?   _15%_

Challenge

19 What percentage of a pound is 36p?   _36%_

20 In a sports club there are 100 children. 54 of them play football.
What percentage of the children do not play football?   _46%_

21 Hamed pours 20ml squash and 80ml water into a glass.
What percentage of the whole drink is squash?   _20%_

22 What is the missing percentage on this clothing label?
No other materials are used.   _53%_

15% cotton
32% polyester
? % silk

23 Fill in the missing numbers.

$\frac{3}{4} = \frac{\boxed{75}}{100} = \boxed{75}$ %

24 A vase can hold 400ml. How many millilitres can 25% or $\frac{1}{4}$ of the vase hold?   _100_ ml

25 Ethan gives 10% of his money to charity each week.
If he earns £100 a week, how much does he give to charity each week? £_10_

26 Use equivalent fractions to help you write 20% as a fraction with the denominator 5. $\frac{1}{5}$

27 The decimal 0.38 is equivalent to the fraction $\frac{38}{100}$.
Is it true that the percentage 38% is equivalent to the decimal 0.38?

Yes ✓   No ☐

28 Write these fractions as percentages.

$\frac{7}{10} = \frac{?}{100} = \boxed{70}$ % $\frac{4}{5} = \frac{?}{100} = \boxed{80}$ % $\frac{7}{20} = \frac{?}{100} = \boxed{35}$ %

81

Understand percentages as fractions and as decimals

Key point

Proportions of a whole can be written as percentages, as decimals or as fractions.

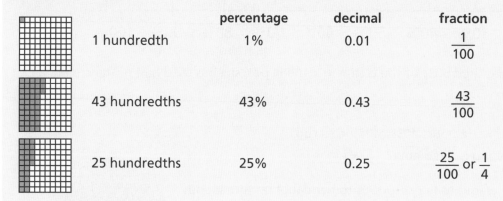

	percentage	decimal	fraction
1 hundredth	1%	0.01	$\frac{1}{100}$
43 hundredths	43%	0.43	$\frac{43}{100}$
25 hundredths	25%	0.25	$\frac{25}{100}$ or $\frac{1}{4}$

Get started

1 True or false? $3\% = \frac{3}{100} = 0.03$

True ✓   False ☐

2 Write 7% as a fraction and as a decimal.

$7\% = \dfrac{7}{100} = \boxed{0.07}$

3 What percentage is equal to 0.5 or $\frac{1}{2}$?

____50%____

4 Write 87 hundredths as a fraction, as a decimal and as a percentage.

$\dfrac{87}{100} = \boxed{0.87} = \boxed{87}$ %

5 True or false? 1% = 0.1

True ☐   False ✓

6 Fill in the missing percentage.

$\dfrac{20}{100} = \boxed{20}$ %

7 What is 20% as a decimal? ___0.2___

8 Given that $25\% = \frac{1}{4}$, what is 25% as a decimal? ___0.25___

0%   25%   50%   75%   100%

Now try these

9 How can 13 hundredths be written as a fraction, as a decimal and as a percentage?

a) fraction ___$\frac{13}{100}$___   **b)** decimal ___0.13___   **c)** percentage ___13%___

10 Tom says that 0.3 is equivalent to 0.30, so 0.3 is equivalent to 30%. Is he correct?   Yes ✓   No ☐

11 Fill in the percentage. $0.9 = \dfrac{9}{10} = \dfrac{?}{100} = \boxed{90}$ %

12 True or false? 75 hundredths of £1 = 75% of £1 = 75p = £0.75   True ✓   False ☐

13 What percentage of a pound is £0.15? ___15%___

14 Write the length that is 61% of one metre as a decimal. ___0.61___ m

15 Write the answer to the question 0.25 + 0.25 as: **a)** a decimal. ___0.5___

b) a percentage. ___50%___   **c)** a fraction. ___$\frac{50}{100}$___   *Also accept $\frac{5}{10}$ or $\frac{1}{2}$*

16 What percentage of a metre is 0.34m? ___34%___

17 The chef poured 0.8l of gravy into a litre jug. Tick the true statements.

$\frac{8}{10}$ of the jug is filled. ✓   80% of the jug is filled. ✓

8% of the jug is filled. ☐   The jug is 20% empty. ✓

18 As a percentage, write what proportion £9 is of £100. ___9%___

Challenge

19 Circle any that are equal to 17%.   (0.17)   0.017 $\frac{17}{10}$ ($\frac{17}{100}$)   1.7

20 Circle the largest proportion.   50% $\frac{3}{4}$ (0.8)   19%

21 True or false? $\frac{1}{5}$ = 5%   True ☐   False ✓

22 Circle all the proportions that are equivalent to 20%.

$\frac{5}{100}$ 0.5   ($\frac{20}{100}$)   0.005   (0.2)   ($\frac{2}{10}$)   0.02   ($\frac{1}{5}$)

23 Find the total mass of these two packets.

Write the answer as a percentage of a kilogram. ___90%___

PASTA 0.45kg   PASTA 0.45kg

24 Ruby scored 132 out of 200 in a test.
Write this as a fraction with the denominator of 100 and then as a percentage.

a) fraction ___$\frac{66}{100}$___   **b)** percentage ___66%___

25 Imogen scored 11 out of 25 in a test.
What is this as a fraction with the denominator of 100, as a percentage and as a decimal?

a) fraction ___$\frac{44}{100}$___   **b)** percentage ___44%___   **c)** decimal ___0.44___

26 Rakesh notices that converting from percentages to decimals is the same as dividing by 100.
So 54% is equal to the decimal made by dividing 54 by 100 = 0.54.

Use his method to write 13.5% as a decimal. 13.5% = ___0.135___

27 The number of rabbits in a forest more than doubles in one year. It increases by 105%.

Write this increase as a decimal. ___1.05___

28 A right angle (90°) is a quarter of a full turn. An angle of 45° is half a right angle.
What percentage of a full turn is an angle of 45°? Circle the answer.

25%   75%   15%   10%   ($12\frac{1}{2}$%)

Relate percentages to 'finding fractions of'

Key point

$50\% = \dfrac{50}{100} = \dfrac{1}{2}$ So, to find 50% of a number, divide by **2**.   50% of 12m = 6m

$25\% = \dfrac{25}{100} = \dfrac{1}{4}$ So, to find 25% of a number, divide by **4**.   25% of 40p = 10p

$10\% = \dfrac{10}{100} = \dfrac{1}{10}$ So, to find 10% of a number, divide by **10**.   10% of 30kg = 3kg

$1\% = \dfrac{1}{100}$ So, to find 1% of a number, divide by **100**.   1% of £400 = £4

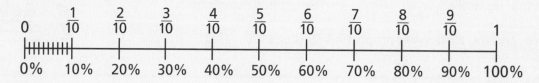

Get started

1   Given that 50% = $\dfrac{1}{2}$, find 50% of £8.

£ ___4___

2   True or false? 50% of 12 is 24.

True ☐   False ✓

3   Given that 25% = $\dfrac{1}{4}$, find 25% of 20p.

___5___ p

4   What is 50% of 50ml? ___25___ ml

5   Find 25% of 40km. ___10___ km

6   What is 10% of 50kg? ___5___ kg

7   What is ten per cent of sixty? Write the answer in words.

_____six_____

8   Find 1% of 700m. ___7___ m

Now try these

9   1 hundredth of 120m is 1.2m. What is 1% of 120m? ___1.2___ m

10   Find the total of 1% of 500 and 10% of 30. ___8___

11   Hamish draws a line that is 10% of the length of line A.

How long is Hamish's line? ___7___ mm

Line A

70mm

12   Fill in the missing percentage. ☐ 50 % ☐ of 200m = 100m

13   Luca draws a line that is 10% longer than line B.

How long is Luca's line? ___33___ cm

Line B

30cm

14   A full turn is 360°. How many degrees are there in 25% of a full turn? ___90___ °

15 25% is one-quarter of a whole. What percentage is three-quarters of a whole? __75%__

16 Find the difference between 25% of 36kg and 10% of 90kg. __0__ kg

17 Zainab takes 25% of the money in each bag.
How much does she take in total? £__19__

£48　£28

18 There are 30 children in a class. How many of the children are girls if:

a) 10% are girls? __3__　b) 20% are girls? __6__　c) 30% are girls? __9__

Challenge

19 $\frac{4}{5} = 80\%$　Use this fact to help you answer the question.

How much less than 4m is 80% of 400cm? __80__ cm

20 | 10% of £270　20% of £150　1% of £3200 |

What is the value of:　a) the largest of these amounts? £__32__

b) the smallest of these amounts? £__27__　c) the total of these amounts? £__89__

21 Dylan is 90% of the height of his brother. His brother is 120cm tall.
How tall is Dylan? __108__ cm

22 20% of an hour is 12 minutes.
What percentage of an hour is 36 minutes? __60%__

23 True or false? 1% of 400g is 4g, so 9% of 400g is 36g.　True ✓　False ☐

24 Find 9% of 700g and add it to 75% of 400g. __363__ g

25 Rose earns £32 000 per year. She pays 25% of the money in tax and 10% into her pension.
How much money does she have left? £20 800

26 Abigail finds 50%, 25%, 10% and 1% of 8400.
She then adds her answers to find 86% of 8400. What is her answer? __7224__

27 At a basketball match 90% of the people are adults. If there are 120 children,
how many people are there altogether at the match? __1200__

28 The width of a rectangle is 40% of its length. Its length is 80mm.
Find the perimeter of the rectangle in centimetres. __22.4__ cm

Solve fraction, decimal and percentage problems

Key point

Proportions of a whole can be described as fractions, as decimals and as percentages. Sometimes it is easier to work with fractions, at other times it is easier to work with percentages or decimals.

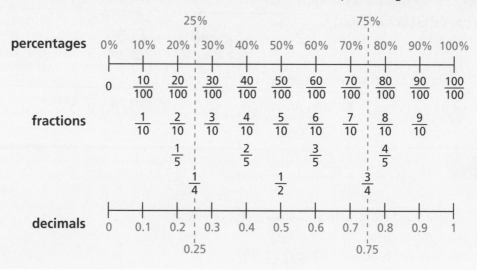

Get started

1 Use the fact that 50% is one-half to help you find 50% of 400ml. ___200___ ml

2 Write $\frac{1}{4}$ as a decimal. ___0.25___

3 How many lots of 0.25m are in one whole metre? ___4___

4 Jade scored 9 out of 10 in a test. What is this score as a percentage? ___90%___

5 Find 25% of 80km. ___20___ km

6 How many lots of 0.1m are in 2m? ___20___

7 True or false? $\frac{37}{100}$m = 37cm = 0.37m
True ✓   False ☐

8 What proportion of £100 is £93? Write the answer as a percentage. ___93%___

Now try these

9 What fraction of a litre is the total amount in these two tubs? $\frac{3}{4}$ or $\frac{75}{100}$ l

 0.5 litres
 0.25 litres

10 How many tenths of a kilogram are equivalent to 70% of a kilogram? ___7___ tenths

11 Fill in the missing numbers in the two sequences.

a) 5%, 10%, 15%, 20%, ___25%___ ,30%, 35% **b)** 0.05, 0.1, 0.15, 0.2, 0.25, ___0.3___ ,0.35

12 Sam scores 73 out of 100 in a test. Julia scores 72% on the same test.

Who has the higher score? ___Sam___

13 How long is a line that is 50% of the length of a line measuring 80mm? ___40___ mm

14 What percentage of a whole turn is a right angle? ___25%___

5   0.35kg of flour and 0.15kg sugar are put into a bowl.
What fraction of a whole kilogram do they weigh in total? $\frac{1}{2}$ or $\frac{50}{100}$ kg

6   Six minutes is equal to one-tenth of an hour.

What percentage of an hour is 18 minutes? __30%__

7   A motorcyclist travels for 4.15km before taking a break and then goes 3.8km after the break.

How much further does he need to go to have travelled 8km altogether? __0.05__ km

18   Find the difference in kilograms between 25% of 32kg and $\frac{1}{10}$ of 160kg. __8__ kg

Challenge

19   Find the total mass of these two boxes of chocolates. Write the answer as:

   a) a percentage of a kilogram. __75%__

   b) a fraction of a kilogram. __$\frac{3}{4}$__ kg   Also accept $\frac{15}{20}$ or $\frac{75}{100}$

20   Erin is $\frac{7}{10}$ of the height of her brother. Her brother is 110cm tall. How tall is Erin? __77__ cm

21   Al earns £20 000 per year. He pays 30% of the money in tax.

How much money does he pay in tax? £__6000__

22   In a test Aswin scored 243 out of 300. Write this as a fraction with a denominator of 100 and then

as a percentage. **a)** fraction __$\frac{81}{100}$__   **b)** percentage __81%__

23   What is the score $\frac{44}{50}$ as a percentage? __88%__

24   Meema takes out 10% of the money in her savings account. She takes out £17.

How much money: **a)** does she have in total? £__170__   **b)** is left in the savings account now? £__153__

25   A can of cola holds 0.3 litres and a bottle of cola holds 55% of a litre. Find the difference between the

amounts of cola in each. Write the answer as a fraction of a litre. __$\frac{1}{4}$__ l

26   A nurse is giving some medicine to a child. The child's dose is 60% of the

adult's dose. If the adult's dose is 80ml, what is the child's dose? __48__ ml

27   Write 870g of 1kg as: **a)** a fraction. __$\frac{87}{100}$__   **b)** a percentage. __87%__   **c)** a decimal. __0.87__

28   This chart shows the number of children who passed their cycling proficiency test at three schools.

	Mickleby School	St James School	Deansgate School
number of children	100	200	500
number of passes	87	184	450

Write each school's number of passes as a percentage of the number of children.

a) Mickleby __87%__   **b)** St James __92%__   **c)** Deansgate __90%__

Check-up test 3

1 Circle which is more.   0.36   (0.63)

1 mark

2 Which of these two numbers has more tenths? Circle it.   0.351   (0.42)

1 mark

3 True or false? 0.704 is greater than 0.8.

True ☐   False ✓

1 mark

4 Ruth jumps 1.7m in the high jump and Will jumps 1.63m.
How much higher does Ruth jump than Will? Give your answer:

a) in metres. _0.07_ m   **b)** in centimetres. _7_ cm

1 mark

5 How many tenths are equal to four-tenths plus two-tenths?

Write the answer in fraction notation. $\frac{6}{10}$

1 mark

6 Add 3.42km and 5.37km. _8.79_ km

1 mark

7 Find the total mass of these three parcels.

_4.625_ kg

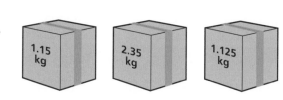

1.15 kg   2.35 kg   1.125 kg

1 mark

8 What decimal is halfway between 0.52 and 0.5? _0.51_

1 mark

9 If 85% of a shape is shaded, what percentage is not shaded? _15%_

1 mark

10 Write A and B as fractions with the denominator 100.

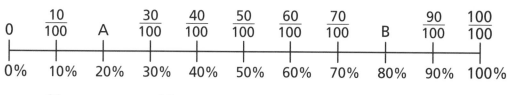

0     $\frac{10}{100}$ A $\frac{30}{100}$ $\frac{40}{100}$ $\frac{50}{100}$ $\frac{60}{100}$ $\frac{70}{100}$ B $\frac{90}{100}$ $\frac{100}{100}$

0%   10%   20%   30%   40%   50%   60%   70%   80%   90%   100%

A = $\frac{20}{100}$ B = $\frac{80}{100}$

1 mark

11 What percentage of one metre is 35cm? _35%_

1 mark

12 Use equivalent fractions to help you write 60%

as a fraction with the denominator 5. $\frac{3}{5}$

1 mark

3   What is 80% as a decimal? ___0.8___

☐ 1 mark

4   True or false? 25 hundredths of £1 = 25% of £1 = 25p = £0.25

True ✓   False ☐

☐ 1 mark

5   Meg pours 0.4 litres of milk into a litre jug. Tick the true statements.

$\frac{4}{10}$ of the jug is filled. ✓   4% of the jug is filled. ☐

40% of the jug is filled. ✓   The jug is 60% empty. ✓

☐ 1 mark

16   Circle the largest proportion.   60% $\left(\frac{3}{4}\right)$ 0.7   49%

☐ 1 mark

17   Find 25% of 60km. ___15___ km

☐ 1 mark

18   Dinesh draws a line that is 10% longer than line A.   Line A

How long is Dinesh's line? ___55___ cm   50cm

☐ 1 mark

19   Find the difference in kilograms between 25% of

24kg and 10% of 70kg. ___1___ kg

☐ 1 mark

20   40% of an hour is 24 minutes.

What percentage of an hour is 48 minutes? ___80%___

☐ 1 mark

21   What proportion of £100 is £86?

Write the answer as a percentage. ___86%___

☐ 1 mark

22   Dan scores 54 out of 100 in a dance competition. Louise scores 56% in the same

competition. Who has the higher score? ___Louise___

☐ 1 mark

23   Six minutes is equal to one-tenth of an hour.

What percentage of an hour is 36 minutes? ___60%___

☐ 1 mark

24   A mother is giving some medicine to her child.
The child's dose is 70% of the adult's dose.
If the adult's dose is 60ml, what is the child's dose? ___42___ ml

☐ 1 mark

Total

☐

24 marks

Final test

Section 1

1 Use < or > to show which is larger. $\frac{6}{10}$ $<$ $\frac{4}{5}$

1 mark

2 Change these fractions to twentieths.
Then write the original fractions in order from smallest to largest.

$\frac{7}{10}$ $\frac{3}{5}$ $\frac{13}{20}$ $\frac{3}{5}$ _____ $\frac{13}{20}$ _____ $\frac{7}{10}$ _____

1 mark

3 Write these fractions in order, smallest first.

$\frac{3}{10}$ $\frac{1}{5}$ $\frac{17}{100}$ $\frac{17}{100}$ _____ $\frac{1}{5}$ _____ $\frac{3}{10}$ _____

1 mark

Section 2

4 How many twelfths are equivalent to $\frac{3}{4}$? ____9____ twelfths

1 mark

5 Fill in the missing number to show an equivalent fraction.

$\frac{18}{21} = \dfrac{6}{7}$

1 mark

6 $\frac{2}{5} = \dfrac{4}{10} = \dfrac{40}{100}$

$\frac{1}{10}$

0        $\frac{2}{5}$ 1

1 mark

Section 3

7 Write the answer as a mixed number. $\frac{4}{7} + \frac{4}{7} = 1\frac{1}{7}$

1 mark

8 Write this improper fraction as a mixed number. $\frac{17}{5} = 3\frac{2}{5}$

1 mark

9 Write this mixed number as an improper fraction. $4\frac{4}{7} = \dfrac{32}{7}$

1 mark

ection 4

10 Answer these.   a) $\frac{3}{9} + \frac{5}{9} + \frac{5}{9} = \boxed{\frac{13}{9}}$ or $\boxed{1 \quad \frac{4}{9}}$ b) $\frac{17}{12} - \frac{10}{12} = \boxed{\frac{7}{12}}$

☐ 1 mark

11 Fill in the missing numbers.

$\frac{3}{10} + \frac{5}{100} = \boxed{\frac{30}{100}} + \frac{5}{100} = \boxed{\frac{35}{100}}$

☐ 1 mark

12 Find the total of $\frac{3}{4} + \frac{3}{20}$. _____ $\frac{18}{20}$ *Also accept* $\frac{9}{10}$

☐ 1 mark

Section 5

13 Mark the answer to $\frac{3}{10} \times 4$ on this number line.

0   1   2

☐ 1 mark

14 $1\frac{1}{4} \times 7 = \boxed{8 \quad \frac{3}{4}}$

☐ 1 mark

15 $3\frac{1}{3} \times 6 = (3 \times 6) + (\frac{1}{3} \times 6) = \boxed{20}$

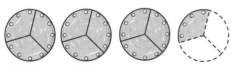

☐ 1 mark

Section 6

16 Write 0.7 as a fraction. _____ $\frac{7}{10}$

☐ 1 mark

17 Write 0.73 as a fraction. _____ $\frac{73}{100}$

☐ 1 mark

18 What fraction of a metre is 0.25m?
Write the fraction with the lowest denominator possible. _____ $\frac{1}{4}$ m

☐ 1 mark

please turn over

Section 7

19 How many thousandths are equal to 0.075?

$0.075 = \dfrac{75}{1000}$

1 mark

20 What is the missing number?

$0.109 = \boxed{109}$ thousandths $= \dfrac{109}{1000}$

1 mark

21 Write $\dfrac{47}{1000}$ as a decimal. _0.047_

1 mark

Section 8

22 Round each decimal to the nearest whole number.

a) 0.6 ___1___

b) 3.4 ___3___

c) 7.47 ___7___

1 mark

23 Round each decimal to the nearest tenth (to one decimal place).

a) 0.63 ___0.6___

b) 3.45 ___3.5___

c) 7.97 ___8.0___

1 mark

24 Circle all the decimals that round to 6.0 when rounded to the nearest tenth.

(5.98)　5.91　6.20　6.31　6.06　(6.02)

1 mark

Section 9

25 Circle the larger number.　0.58　(0.6)

1 mark

26 Use < or > to show which is larger. 0.91 $\boxed{>}$ 0.908

1 mark

27 Put these decimals in order from smallest to largest.

0.3　0.331　0.33　0.03　0.003

_0.003_　_0.03_　_0.3_　_0.33_　_0.331_

1 mark

ection 10

8   Add 0.7km and 1.6km.   <u>2.3</u>   km

☐ 1 mark

9   Find the total mass of these three bags. 

  <u>4.875</u> kg

☐ 1 mark

0   How much more does the white bottle hold than the turquoise bottle?

Give your answer: **a)** in litres.   <u>0.019</u> l

                b) in millilitres.   <u>19</u>   ml

0.09 litre   0.109 litre

☐ 1 mark

ection 11

1   Write 7% as a fraction and then as a decimal.

$7\% = \boxed{\dfrac{7}{100}} = \boxed{0.07}$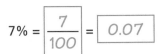

☐ 1 mark

2   Circle those that are equal to 59%.   (0.59)   0.059 $\dfrac{59}{10}$ $\left(\dfrac{59}{100}\right)$ 5.9

☐ 1 mark

3   Write this as a percentage and as a decimal. $\dfrac{4}{5} = \dfrac{?}{100}$

   a) percentage   <u>80%</u>   **b)** decimal   <u>0.8</u>

☐ 1 mark

ection 12

4   Find 25% of 44km.   <u>11</u>   km

☐ 1 mark

5   0.35kg of flour and 0.15kg sugar are put into a bowl.
What percentage of a kilogram do they weigh in total?   <u>50%</u>

☐ 1 mark

36   Emily is 80% of the height of her brother.

Her brother is 120cm tall. How tall is Emily?   <u>96</u>   cm

☐ 1 mark

Total

☐

36 marks

End of test

Pupil progress chart

Pupil's name _____   Class / set _____

Unit	Get started		Now try these		Challenge		Total	
1		8		10		10		28
2		8		10		10		28
3		8		10		10		28
4		8		10		10		28
5		8		10		10		28
6		8		10		10		28
Check-up test 1								24
7		8		10		10		28
8		8		10		10		28
9		8		10		10		28
10		8		10		10		28
11		8		10		10		28
12		8		10		10		28
Check-up test 2								24
13		8		10		10		28
14		8		10		10		28
15		8		10		10		28
16		8		10		10		28
17		8		10		10		28
18		8		10		10		28
Check-up test 3								24

Final test group record sheet

Pupil's name	Y5/F1			Y5/F2			Y5/F3			Y5/F4			Y5/F5			Y5/F6			Y5/F7			Y5/F8			Y5/F9			Y5/F10			Y5/F11			Y5/F12			Total
	1	2	3	4	5	6	7	8	9	10	11	12	13	14	15	16	17	18	19	20	21	22	23	24	25	26	27	28	29	30	31	32	33	34	35	36	
																																					/36
																																					/36

Full list of books in the Fractions, Decimals and Percentages series

Pupil books

Fractions 1	ISBN 978 0 7217 1375 5
Fractions 2	ISBN 978 0 7217 1377 9
Fractions 3	ISBN 978 0 7217 1379 3
Fractions 4	ISBN 978 0 7217 1381 6
Fractions 5	ISBN 978 0 7217 1383 0
Fractions 6	ISBN 978 0 7217 1385 4

Teacher's guides

Fractions 1 Teacher's Guide	ISBN 978 0 7217 1376 2
Fractions 2 Teacher's Guide	ISBN 978 0 7217 1378 6
Fractions 3 Teacher's Guide	ISBN 978 0 7217 1380 9
Fractions 4 Teacher's Guide	ISBN 978 0 7217 1382 3
Fractions 5 Teacher's Guide	ISBN 978 0 7217 1384 7
Fractions 6 Teacher's Guide	ISBN 978 0 7217 1386 1

Free downloads available from the Schofield & Sims website

A selection of free downloads is available from the Schofield & Sims website (www.schofieldandsims.co.uk/free-downloads). These may be used to further enhance the effectiveness of the programme. The downloads add to the range of print materials supplied in the teacher's guides.

- **Graphics** slides containing the visual elements from each teacher's guide unit provided as Microsoft PowerPoint® presentations.

- **Go deeper investigations** providing additional extension material to develop problem-solving and reasoning skills.

- **Additional resources** including a fraction wall, a comparison chart and number lines to support learning and teaching.